HEINEMANN MODULAR MATHEMATICS

for

LONDON AS AND A-LEVEL

Statistics 2

Greg Attwood Gill Dyer

1 2 3 4 5 6

Heinemann Educational Publishers,
Halley Court, Jordan Hill, Oxford OX2 8EJ
a division of Reed Educational & Professional Publishing Ltd

MELBOURNE AUCKLAND FLORENCE PRAGUE MADRID
ATHENS SINGAPORE TOKYO SÃO PAULO CHICAGO
PORTSMOUTH (NH) MEXICO IBADAN GABORONE
JOHANNESBURG KAMPALA NAIROBI

First published 1995

96 10 9 8 7 6 5 4 3

ISBN 0 435 51812 7

Original design by Geoffrey Wadsley: additional design work by Jim Turner

Typeset by Keyword Typesetting Services Limited, Wallington, Surrey

Printed in Great Britain by the Bath Press, Avon

Acknowledgements:

The publisher's and authors' thanks are due to the University of London Examinations and Assessment Council (ULEAC) for permission to reproduce questions from past examination papers. These are marked with an [L].

The answers have been provided by the authors and are not the responsibility of the examining board.

The publishers would also like to thank the University of London Examination and Assessment Council (ULEAC) for permission to reproduce the following mathematical tables:
Table 1 Binomial cumulative distribution function,
Table 2 Poisson cumulative distribution function,
Table 3 The Normal distribution function,
Table 4 Percentage points of the Normal distribution.
Table 5 Percentage points of the χ^2 distribution
Table 6 Critical values for correlation coefficients
Table 7 Random numbers

About this book

This book is designed to provide you with the best preparation possible for your London Modular Mathematics T2 examination. The series authors are examiners and exam moderators themselves and have a good understanding of the exam board's requirements.

Finding your way around

To help to find your way around when you are studying and revising use the:

- **edge marks** (shown on the front page) – these help you to get to the right chapter quickly;
- **contents list** – this lists the headings that identify key syllabus ideas covered in the book so you can turn straight to them;
- **index** – if you need to find a topic the **bold** number shows where to find the main entry on a topic.

Remembering key ideas

We have provided clear explanations of the key ideas and techniques you need throughout the book. Key ideas you need to remember are listed in a **summary of key points** at the end of each chapter and marked like this in the chapters:

■ **Standard error of the mean is $\frac{\sigma}{\sqrt{n}}$ or $\frac{s}{\sqrt{n}}$.**

Exercises and exam questions

In this book questions are carefully graded so they increase in difficulty and gradually bring you up to exam standard.

- **past exam questions** are marked with an L;
- **review exercises** on pages 74 and 183 help you practise answering questions from several areas of mathematics at once, as in the real exam;
- **exam style practice paper** – this is designed to help you prepare for the exam itself;
- **answers** are included at the end of the book – use them to check your work.

Contents

Sampling methods 1

1.1 Collecting data

Before you can get information from statistical data you must first collect the data. We will be looking at a number of methods of collecting data in this chapter.

In Book T1 we defined data as 'a series of observations, measurements or facts', and the thing being observed or measured we called the variate. The collection of individuals or items under discussion was called the population. We went further and defined a sample as 'a selection of individual items or members of the population'. The advantages and disadvantages of taking a sample were also explained in Book T1.

Briefly, the advantages are:

- it is generally cheaper
- it can be taken as representative of the whole population; that is, it will have the same distribution.

The disadvantage is:

- there is some uncertainty as a result of natural variation and bias.

1.2 Taking a census

If every member of a population is observed or measured it is called taking a **census**.

For example, if you wanted to find the mean height of students in a certain sixth form, you could measure each student. You would then be taking a census. Perhaps the best known census is that conducted by the British Government. In this census every known householder in Great Britain receives a census form every 10 years. Each householder is required by law to complete and return the form by a certain date. The census form records a variety of information, such as the number of people present, their ages, and so on.

A census is used if:

- the size of the population is small, or if
- extreme accuracy is required.

The advantage of using a census is that:

- it should give a completely accurate result. (This may be necessary where governments are planning housing requirements, school programmes, new hospitals, and so on, or in industry where a component is being tested for safety.)

The disadvantages of a census are that:

- it is very time consuming and expensive
- it cannot be used when the testing process is to destruction (for example, testing an apple for sweetness)
- the information is difficult to process because there is so much of it.

Example 1

Give a brief explanation and an example of the use of (a) a census (b) a sample survey. [L]

(a) Census – every member of the population is observed.
Example: 10-year national census

(b) Sample survey – a small portion of the population is observed.
Example: opinion polls

1.3 Sampling

Suppose in the sixth form mentioned in section 1.2 there were 400 students. Even though this number is quite small it would take a long time to conduct a census by measuring the height of each student. A sampling frame of 50 would give you a good estimate of the mean of their heights provided that you select your sample so that it is free from bias. To do this you must make sure that your selection is truly random.

The size of a sample (the number of people or units sampled) does not depend on the size of the population. It depends on the accuracy you require and the resources you are willing to allocate to data collection. A large sample will usually be more accurate than a small one, but will need greater resources. The number of items sampled may also be affected by the nature of the population: if the population is very variable you will require a larger sample size than you would if the population were more uniform.

We will now look at some methods of sampling.

1.4 Simple random sampling

Suppose a population contains N sampling units and you require a sample of n of them. A sample of size n is called a **simple random sample** if every other possible sample of size n has an equal chance of being selected. In practice this is achieved by giving each member of the total population an equal chance of being selected.

Two well known examples of random sampling are ERNIE (Electronic Random Number Indicating Equipment), which is used to select winning numbers on Premium Bonds, and the selection of numbers for the National Lottery. Both of these are run by very big organisations and can justify the expense of using special equipment.

There are two simple techniques that are commonly used and that do not require elaborate equipment:

- lottery or ticket sampling
- random number sampling.

In **lottery sampling** you construct a model of the population and then sample the model. Each element of the population is identified by some distinct characteristic, such as a name or number, and this is written on a ticket. The tickets are put into a container and the required number of tickets is withdrawn. If you wanted a sample size of 50 you would withdraw 50 tickets. The elements of the population corresponding to the tickets are then selected. This method is satisfactory for sampling frames (ordered and numbered lists of data) with a small number of sampling elements.

In **random number sampling** each element of the population is assigned a number, for example, 000,001, . . . , 009,010, . . . 099,100, . . . , 399. Once you have done this you can use tables of random sampling numbers such as the one at the back of this book (Table 7 in the Appendix). These tables contain 1000 or more digits, that is to say, integers starting from 0, i.e. 0,1,2,3,4,5,6,7,8,9. The table is constructed with great care so that each digit is equally likely to appear.

The fourth and fifth columns from the left of Table 7 begin:

```
39 05   97 96
09 46   91 33
01 06   64 65
18 40   97 79
70 56   30 15
```

97 36 56 61
99 15 56 86
56 14 71 23
54 77 66 29
57 01 87 33

To obtain a sample of size 50 from our sixth form you would need an alphabetic list of names to which you can assign numbers, and a sample of 50 numbers between 000 and 399 inclusive. Using the table you could take the first three digits on each line.

39 0|5
09 4|6
01 0|6
18 4|0
70 5|6

This gives you the numbers 390, 094, 010, 184, 705, etc. A number such as 705 is ignored as it does not lie in the range 000 to 399. When the bottom of the table is reached you could start again at the top with the next three unused digits along the top row (597 in this case). Once you have your 50 numbers, you go back to the population and select the corresponding students. Although we started at the top of the table and read downwards it is better to start at a randomly selected place in the table, and you may travel in any direction.

To save time you could allocate a second set of numbers to each item or individual so that you do not have to discard so many numbers. You must make sure that each item has the same chance of selection. In the above case you would allocate two numbers to each and not three numbers to some and two numbers to others. For example, you could use:

001 and 401 for the first on the list
002 and 402 for the second on the list
....
....
400 and 800 for the last on the list,

and ignore numbers greater than 800.

Nowadays computers and calculators can produce lists of random numbers.

The advantages of random number sampling are:

- the numbers are truly random and free from bias
- it is easy to use
- each number has a known equal chance of selection.

The disadvantage is:

- it is not suitable where the sample size is large.

Example 2

Describe what is meant by a simple random sample, and give one advantage and one disadvantage associated with it.

A simple random sample is one in which each member of the population has an equal chance of being selected.

It is free from bias.

It is not suitable for large sample sizes.

Example 3

Explain how to use random number tables to select a sample of 12 people from a population of 100.

Allocate a two-digit number to each person, starting at 00 and ending at 99.

Select a random starting point in the table (say, 5th column and 7th row). Select 12 random numbers (56, 86, 80, 57, 11, 78, 40, 23, 58, 40, 86, 14 by reading across or 56, 71, 66, 87, 09, 11, 48, 14, 33, 79, 12, 02, by reading vertically).

Go back to the original population and select the people corresponding to these numbers.

1.5 Systematic sampling

A sample that is obtained by choosing at regular intervals from an ordered list is called a **systematic sample**.

In the case of our sixth form, you could take every eighth student from an alphabetical list in order to get a sample size of 50 from 400. Generally, if you want to select a sample of size n from a population of size N then you select an interval of $\frac{N}{n}$. You could of course adjust your sample size (n) so that it divides N exactly, otherwise it would not be random.

To overcome the objection that the first name is bound to be selected, you can introduce a direct element of randomness by selecting the first name as if it were a random sample. Pick a number at random between 1 and 8, and if it is, say, the number 3, start at the third name on the list.

When you are selecting the interval, it is possible to introduce bias if you are not careful. Suppose you were investigating the mean rainfall each month over 100 years: an interval of 12 months would introduce bias, as you would be looking at the same month in each year.

Systematic sampling is used when:

- the population is too large for simple random number sampling.

The advantages of systematic sampling are:

- it is simple to use
- it is suitable for large samples.

The disadvantage is:

- it is only random if the ordered list is truly random.

1.6 Stratified sampling

This is a form of random sampling in which the population is divided into groups or categories which are mutually exclusive, so no individual or item can be in two groups. These groups are called **strata** (singular: stratum). The strata would be decided according to one or more criteria such as sex, age, religion and so on.

Within each of these strata a simple random sample is selected. If the same proportion of each stratum is taken, then each stratum will be represented in the correct proportion in the overall result.

For example, if the sixth form had 160 in the upper sixth and 240 in the lower sixth then the natural strata would be upper and lower sixth, and for a sample size of 50 we would take $\frac{50}{400}$ $(\frac{1}{8})$ of each, that is, 30 lower and 20 upper sixth formers. In this way we can be sure of getting a balanced view with upper and lower sixth both proportionately represented, and with each student having an equal chance of being selected.

Stratified sampling is used when:

- the sample is large and
- the population divides naturally into mutually exclusive groups.

The advantages of stratified sampling are:

- it can give more accurate estimates than simple random sampling where there are **clear strata present** .
- it also gives separate estimates for the strata.

The disadvantages are:

- within the strata, the problems are the same as for any simple random sample
- if the strata are not clearly defined they may overlap.

1.7 Sampling with and without replacement

If the unit selected at each draw is replaced into the population before the next draw, then it can appear more than once in the sample. This is known as **sampling with replacement**. If the unit is not replaced, so only those units not previously selected are eligible for the next draw, then it is known as **sampling without replacement**.

Simple random sampling is sampling without replacement. If random sampling takes place with replacement then it is **unrestricted random sampling**.

1.8 Other sampling methods

The chief characteristic of simple, systematic and stratified sampling is that every individual has a known probability of being included in the sample – the sample is random. Non-random sampling methods are used when it is not possible to use random methods, for example, when the whole population is not known. There are two common non-random methods:

(i) **Quota sampling** in which an interviewer is instructed to interview a certain number of people with chosen characteristics.
(ii) **Cluster sampling** in which you divide the population you want to study into smaller groups called clusters. Then you choose some of these clusters of data by random methods and examine every member of the chosen clusters.

Non-random sampling will not be studied in more detail in this course.

1.9 Primary and secondary sources of data

In chapter 6 we will be discussing the problem of doing a statistical project and the question will arise as to whether to use primary or secondary data.

By **primary data** we mean data that is collected by or on behalf of the person who is going to use the data. For example, if you collect your own data for your project they will be primary data.

By **secondary data** we mean data that is not collected by the person who is to use the data. They are second hand. For example, if you use data from the government census in your project they are secondary data.

Primary data have the advantages that:

- the collection method is known
- the accuracy is known
- the exact data needed are collected.

The disadvantage is:

- it is costly in time and effort.

Secondary data have the advantages that:

- they are cheap to obtain – government publications are relatively cheap
- a large quantity of data is available
- much of the data have been collected for years and can be used to plot trends.

The disadvantages are:

- the collection method may not be known
- the accuracy may not be known
- the data may not be ideal for the purpose to which they are to be put.

Exercise 1A

1 Explain briefly what is meant by the term sampling and give three advantages of taking a sample.

2 Define what is meant by a census. By referring to specific examples, suggest two reasons why a census might be used.

3 A factory makes safety harnesses for climbers and has an order to supply 3000 harnesses. The buyer wishes to know that the load at which the harness breaks exceeds a certain figure. Suggest a reason why a census would not be used for this purpose.

4 Explain:

(a) why a sample might be preferred to a census

(b) what you understand by a sampling frame

(c) what effect the size of the population has on the size of the sampling frame

(d) what effect the variability of the population has on the size of the sampling frame.

5 Explain briefly the difference between a census and a sample survey.

Write brief notes on:

(a) simple random sampling

(b) stratified sampling

(c) systematic sampling.

Your notes should include the definition, practical implications and any advantages and disadvantages associated with each method of sampling. [L]

6 Using the random numbers 4 and 3 to give you the column and line respectively in the random number table (Table 7, p. 210), select a sample of size 6 from the numbers:

(a) 0–99

(b) 50–150

(c) 1–600

7 A company wishes to do consumer marketing research using a certain town. Suggest a suitable sampling frame and describe in detail a way of selecting a sample of 400 people aged over 21.

8 Explain the purpose of stratification in carrying out a sample survey.

9 A survey is to be done on the adult population of a certain city suburb, the population of which is 2000. An ordered list of the inhabitants is available.

(a) What sampling method would you use and why?

(b) What condition would have to be applied to your ordered list if the selection is to be truly random?

10 In a marketing sample survey the sales of cigarettes in a variety of outlets is to be investigated. The outlets consist of small kiosks selling cigarettes and tobacco only, tobacconists shops that sell cigarettes and related products and shops that sell cigarettes and other unrelated products.

(a) Suggest the most suitable form of taking a random sample.

(b) Explain how you would conduct the sample survey.

(c) What are the advantages and disadvantages of the method chosen?

11 (a) Explain briefly:

(i) why it is often desirable to take samples

(ii) what you understand by a sampling frame.

(b) State two circumstances when you would consider using

(i) systematic sampling

(ii) stratification

when sampling from a population.

SUMMARY OF KEY POINTS

1 A census observes or measures every member of a population.

2 A random sample is one in which every member of the population has an equal chance of being selected.

3 In lottery sampling, tickets that identify each element of the population are placed into a container and the required number in the sample are withdrawn.

4 In random number sampling, each element is given a number and the numbers of the required elements are read from a random number table.

5 In systematic sampling the required elements are chosen at regular intervals from an ordered list.

6 In stratified sampling the population is divided into mutually exclusive strata and a random sample is taken from each.

Estimation, confidence intervals and tests

2

The doctors say Jim is of average height. In fact, he is actually 1.84 m tall; but how can we find the average height of adult men? John was also told that he was of average height, but he is 1.88 m tall. Does this mean that the doctors are using a range of values to describe average height, say from 1.80 to 1.90 m perhaps? Paul is 1.92 m tall but he claims to be of average height. How can we test this claim, and what basis could we give for saying that Paul was *above* average height? In this chapter we shall examine ways of finding estimates and ranges of values for estimates, as well as looking at a method of testing claims like Paul's that uses probability.

2.1 Statistics and sampling distributions

A new company is thinking of selling trendy raincoats to students in a sixth form college. The company would like to know something about the heights of students in the college and in particular the *mean* height of a student. Unfortunately, the size of the college means that it is not practical to measure every student in the college and so a method of *estimating* this mean height is required. The heights of the students at the college form a large **population**. We can call the mean height of the students μ(mu) and the standard deviation of the heights of the students σ(sigma). But the company does not know the values of μ and σ and it cannot afford the time or money to find them. As in Book T1, we shall call μ and σ **population parameters**: that is, they are the mean and standard deviation for the *whole population*. Greek letters are used to denote population parameters.

Population of heights of students

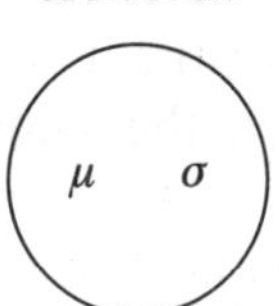

The problem that the company has is how to *estimate* the parameter μ. In order to answer this question we take a **sample** from the population. In chapter 1 several methods of sampling are discussed but the theory of estimation that is used in this course assumes that a **simple random sample of size *n*** is used.

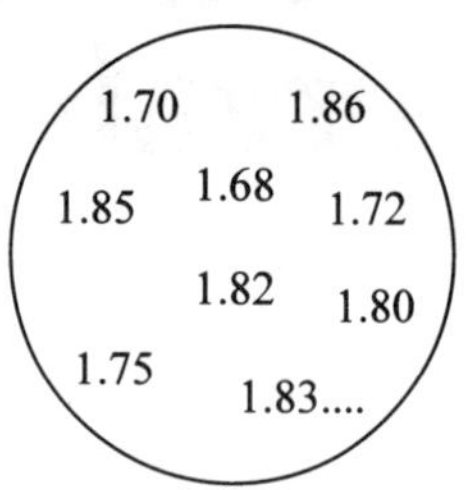

Consider the following example. Suppose that some of the students in the college are

John, Steve, Greg, Gordon, Jill, Barbara, Carol, Geoff, Graham, . . .

with heights

1.70 m, 1.68 m, 1.85 m, 1.86 m, 1.75 m, 1.72 m, 1.80 m, 1.83 m, 1.82 m, . . .

respectively and that we wish to take a sample of size 3. The dots indicate that the population consists of many more values than those given here and, for the purposes of our sample, the population can be treated as though it were of infinite size. It is important to remember that the population is a population of *heights* and therefore the sample will be a collection of heights.

In this chapter our populations will always consist of numbers and so, therefore, will any samples since a sample is simply a *subset* of the population. This use of the term sample is perhaps slightly different to that in common usage. If you asked a non-statistical friend to select a sample of size 3 from the college they would probably give you the names of three students: for example, John, Geoff and Carol. But here we want the heights of the students, namely 1.70 m, 1.83 m and 1.80 m, and we could write $x_1 = 1.70$, $x_2 = 1.83$ and $x_3 = 1.80$ where x_i is the ith member of the sample. If you now were to select a random sample of size 3 from the above population you would almost certainly obtain different values for x_1, x_2 and x_3. In order to describe and refer to such a sample it is usual to introduce the random variables X_1, X_2 and X_3 to refer to the first, second and third members of the sample, respectively. As the members of the sample will always be numbers, it makes sense to refer to the ith member of the sample as a random variable X_i (you will recall from Book T1, chapter 6, that a random variable must always have a numerical value).

Given a random variable, the first question you should ask is, what is its distribution? The random variable X_1 is simply a randomly selected member of the population, as indeed are all the X_i. So X_1, and each of the X_i will have the *same distribution as the population* from which the sample is taken. So in particular $\mathrm{E}(X_i) = \mu$ and $\mathrm{Var}(X_i) = \sigma^2$ for every member of the sample. These results will be used in the next section. Since the sample you are dealing with is a simple random sample, each of the X_i will also be an *independent* random variable.

In this chapter (as in chapter 6 of Book T1) we shall distinguish between the random variable X_i, representing the ith observation in a sample, and the value x_i of the observation in a *specific case*. So, for example, if the fourth person measured was 1.85 m tall then $x_4 = 1.85$. In summary, we have:

- **A simple random sample of size n consists of the observations $X_1, X_2, X_3, \ldots X_n$ from a population where the X_i**
  – are independent random variables
  – have the same distribution as the population.

It is usual practice to drop the term 'simple' and refer to such a sample as a **random sample.**

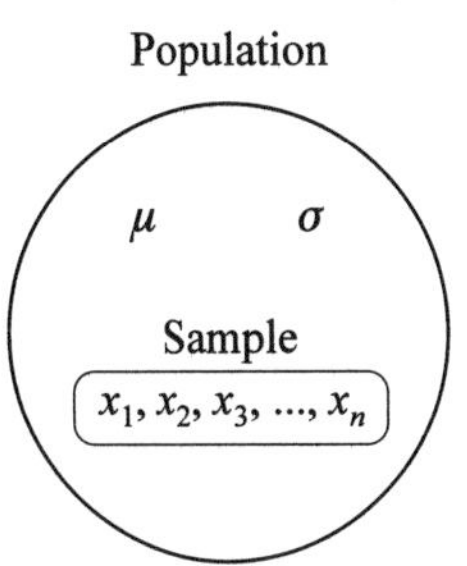

So how can you use the sample to estimate the parameters of the population? The only information available to you is the observations in the sample and you must use some function of the sample values to estimate the parameters for the population. Such a function is called a **statistic.**

- **If $X_1, X_2, X_3, \ldots X_n$ is a random sample of size n from some population then a statistic T is a random variable consisting of any function of the X_i that involves no other quantities.**

There are certain statistics that were introduced in Book T1 (chapter 4), namely

$$\bar{X} = \frac{\sum X}{n} \quad \text{and} \quad S^2 = \frac{\sum(X - \bar{X})^2}{n - 1}$$

and these are particularly important statistics, as you will see in a later section. It is worth stressing that a statistic should not be a function involving any unknown quantities and the function $\frac{\sum(X - \mu)^2}{n}$, which was also introduced in Book T1, is *not* a statistic as it involves the parameter μ.

Since it is possible to repeat the process of taking a sample, the particular value of a statistic T in a specific case, namely t, will be different for each sample. If all possible samples are taken then these values will form a probability distribution called the **sampling distribution of T.**

- **The distribution of the X_i (which is the same as the distribution of the population) will determine the distribution of a statistic T. This is called the sampling distribution of the statistic.**

In chapter 8 of Book T1 you saw that if $X_1 \sim \text{N}(\mu, \sigma^2)$ and $X_2 \sim \text{N}(\mu, \sigma^2)$ then $(X_1 + X_2) \sim \text{N}(\mu + \mu, \sigma^2 + \sigma^2)$, i.e.

$$(X_1 + X_2) \sim \text{N}(2\mu, [\sqrt{2}\sigma]^2)$$

and this property of the normal distribution is one reason why it is of great importance in the theory of sampling.

Example 1

The weights, in grams, of a consignment of apples are normally distributed with a mean μ and standard deviation 4. A sample of size 25 is taken and the statistics R and T are calculated as follows:

$$R = X_{25} - X_1 \quad \text{and} \quad T = X_1 + X_2 + \ldots + X_{25}$$

Find the distributions of R and T.

The sample will be $X_1, X_2, \ldots X_{25}$ where each $X_i \sim \text{N}(\mu, 4^2)$.

Now: $\quad R = X_{25} - X_1 \Rightarrow R \sim \text{N}(\mu - \mu, 4^2 + 4^2)$

that is: $\quad R \sim \text{N}(0, [4\sqrt{2}]^2)$

Also $\quad T = X_1 + X_2 + \ldots + X_{25}$

so: $\quad T \sim \text{N}(25\mu, 25 \times 4^2)$

or $\quad T \sim \text{N}(25\mu, 20^2)$

Example 2

A large bag contains counters. Sixty per cent of the counters have the number 0 on them and forty per cent have the number 1.

(a) Find the mean μ and variance σ^2 for this population of counters.

A simple random sample of size 3 is taken from this population.

(b) List all possible samples.

(c) Find the sampling distribution for the mean $\bar{X} = \dfrac{X_1 + X_2 + X_3}{3}$

(d) Hence find $\text{E}(\bar{X})$ and $\text{Var}(\bar{X})$.

(e) Find the sampling distribution for the mode M.

(f) Hence find $\text{E}(M)$ and $\text{Var}(M)$.

(a) The distribution of the population is

X:	0	1
p(x):	$\frac{3}{5}$	$\frac{2}{5}$

$$\mu = \text{E}(x) = \sum_{\forall x} x\text{P}(X = x) = 0 + \tfrac{2}{5} \Rightarrow \mu = \tfrac{2}{5}$$

$$\sigma^2 = \text{Var}(X) = \sum_{\forall x} x^2\text{P}(X = x) - \mu^2 = 0 + 1^2 \cdot \tfrac{2}{5} - \tfrac{4}{25} \Rightarrow \sigma^2 = \tfrac{6}{25}$$

(b) The possible samples are

$$(0,0,0)$$
$$(1,0,0)\ (0,1,0)\ (0,0,1)$$
$$(1,1,0)\ (1,0,1)\ (0,1,1)$$
$$(1,1,1)$$

(c) $P(\bar{X}=0) = (\frac{3}{5})^3 = \frac{27}{125}$ i.e. the (0,0,0) case

$P(\bar{X}=\frac{1}{3}) = 3 \cdot \frac{2}{5} \cdot (\frac{3}{5})^2 = \frac{54}{125}$ i.e. the (1,0,0); (0,1,0); (0,0,1) cases

$P(\bar{X}=\frac{2}{3}) = 3 \cdot (\frac{2}{5})^2 \cdot \frac{3}{5} = \frac{36}{125}$ i.e. the (1,1,0); (1,0,1); (0,1,1) cases

$P(\bar{X}=1) = (\frac{2}{5})^3 = \frac{8}{125}$ i.e. the (1,1,1) case.

So the distribution for $\bar{X}$ is

$\bar{X}$:	0	$\frac{1}{3}$	$\frac{2}{3}$	1
$p(\bar{x})$:	$\frac{27}{125}$	$\frac{54}{125}$	$\frac{36}{125}$	$\frac{8}{125}$

(d) $E(\bar{X}) = 0 + \frac{1}{3} \times \frac{54}{125} + \frac{2}{3} \times \frac{36}{125} + 1 \times \frac{8}{125} = \frac{18+24+8}{125} = \frac{2}{5}$

$\text{Var}(\bar{X}) = 0 + \frac{1}{9} \times \frac{54}{125} + \frac{4}{9} \times \frac{36}{125} + 1 \times \frac{8}{125} - \frac{4}{25} = \frac{6+16+8}{125} - \frac{20}{125} = \frac{2}{25}$

(e) The mode M can take values 0 or 1.

$P(M=0) = \frac{27}{125} + \frac{54}{125} = \frac{81}{125}$ [i.e. cases (0,0,0); (1,0,0); (0,1,0); (0,0,1)]

and $P(M=1) = \frac{44}{125}$ [i.e. the other cases]

so the distribution of M is

M:	0	1
$p(m)$:	$\frac{81}{125}$	$\frac{44}{125}$

(f) $E(M) = 0 + 1 \times \frac{44}{125} = \frac{44}{125}$

and $\text{Var}(M) = 0 + 1 \times \frac{44}{125} - (\frac{44}{125})^2 = 0.228$

Notice that $E(\bar{X}) = \mu$ but $E(M) \neq \mu$ and that neither $E(\bar{X})$ nor $E(M)$ are equal to the population mode, which is of course zero as 60% of the counters have a zero on them. These results will be examined in further detail in the next section.

Exercise 2A

1 The weights of apples from a certain orchard are assumed to have mean μ and standard deviation σ. A sample of 30 apples was taken and their weights recorded. If the sample is represented by $X_1, X_2, \ldots X_{30}$ state whether or not the following are statistics.

(a) $\dfrac{X_1 + X_{30}}{2}$ (b) $\dfrac{\Sigma X}{30}$ (c) $\dfrac{\Sigma|X - \mu|}{30}$

(d) $\dfrac{\Sigma(X - \bar{X})^2}{30}$ (e) $\dfrac{\Sigma X^2}{30} - \sigma^2$ (f) $\sum\left(\dfrac{X - \mu}{\sigma}\right)$

(g) $\text{Max}\{X_1, X_2, X_3, \ldots X_{30}\}$

2 The lengths of nails produced by a certain machine are normally distributed with a mean μ and standard deviation σ. A random sample of 10 nails is taken and their lengths $\{X_1, X_2, X_3, \ldots X_{10}\}$ are measured.

(i) Write down the distributions of the following:

(a) $\sum_{1}^{10} X_i$ (b) $\dfrac{2X_1 + 3X_{10}}{5}$ (c) $\sum_{1}^{10}(X_i - \mu)$

(d) $\bar{X}$ (e) $\sum_{1}^{5} X_i - \sum_{6}^{10} X_i$ (f) $\sum_{1}^{10}\left(\dfrac{X_i - \mu}{\sigma}\right)$

(ii) State which of the above are statistics.

3 A machine produces components for an electrical appliance but 5% of these are defective. A random sample of 20 components are checked and the random variables $X_i : i = 1, 2, \ldots 20$ are defined as follows:

$$X_i = \begin{cases} 1 & \text{if the } i\text{th component is defective} \\ 0 & \text{if the } i\text{th component is not defective} \end{cases}$$

(a) Write down the distribution for ΣX_i, i.e. the total number of defectives in the sample.

(b) Find $\text{P}(\Sigma X_i \leqslant 2)$.

(c) Find $\text{E}(\Sigma X_i)$ and $\text{Var}(\Sigma X_i)$.

(d) Find $\text{E}(\bar{X})$ and $\text{Var}(\bar{X})$.

4 Repeat question 3 if the proportion that are defective is p.

5 A quarter of the pupils in a large school come to school by bus. A random sample of 10 pupils is selected and the random variables X_i are defined as follows

$$X_i = \begin{cases} 1 & \text{if the pupil comes to school by bus} \\ 0 & \text{otherwise} \end{cases}$$

(a) Write down the distribution for ΣX_i the total number of pupils in the sample who come to school by bus.

(b) Find $\text{P}(\Sigma X \leqslant 2)$ and $\text{P}(\Sigma X > 6)$.

(c) Find $E(\Sigma X_i)$ and $Var(\Sigma X_i)$.

(d) Find $E(\bar{X})$ and $Var(\bar{X})$.

6 A large bag of coins contains 1p, 5p and 10p coins in the ratio 3 : 2 : 1.

(a) Find the mean μ and the variance σ^2 for the value of coins in this population.

A random sample of two coins is taken and their values X_1 and X_2 are recorded.

(b) List all possible samples.

(c) Find the sampling distribution for the mean $\bar{X} = \dfrac{X_1 + X_2}{2}$.

(d) Hence find $E(\bar{X})$ and $Var(\bar{X})$.

7 A manufacturer of self-assembly furniture required bolts of two lengths, 5 cm and 10 cm, in the ratio 3 : 1 respectively.

(a) Find the mean μ and the variance σ^2 for the lengths of bolts in this population. A random sample of three bolts is selected from a large box containing bolts in the required ratio.

(b) List all possible samples.

(c) Find the sampling distribution for the mean $\bar{X}$.

(d) Hence find $E(\bar{X})$ and $Var(\bar{X})$.

(e) Find the sampling distribution for the mode M.

(f) Hence find $E(M)$ and $Var(M)$.

8 A large bag of counters has 25% with the number 0 on, 25% with the number 2 on and 50% with the number 1.

(a) Find the mean μ and the variance σ^2 for this population of counters.

A random sample of size 3 is taken from the bag.

(b) List all possible samples.

(c) Find the sampling distribution for the mean $\bar{X}$.

(d) Hence find $E(\bar{X})$ and $Var(\bar{X})$.

(e) Find the sampling distribution for the median N.

(f) Hence find $E(N)$ and $Var(N)$.

2.2 Unbiased estimates

At the start of this chapter we were considering the problem of trying to estimate the mean height of students in a sixth form college. If you take a random sample of size n then you can find various statistics. The question is, are any of these statistics useful in estimating the population parameters?

A statistic that is used to estimate a population parameter is called an **estimator**; the particular value of this estimator generated by a particular sample is called an **estimate**. Following example 2, page 14, we noted that the sample mean $\bar{X}$ had the property $E(\bar{X}) = \mu$, so if you use $\bar{X}$ as an estimator for μ then 'on average' it will give you the mean μ. Such an estimator is called **unbiased**.

- **If a statistic T is used as an estimator for a population parameter θ and $E(T) = \theta$ then T is an unbiased estimator for θ.**

It seems obvious that unbiasedness is a desirable feature to have in an estimator, but not all estimators possess this property. In example 2 on page 14 we found two statistics based on samples of size 3 from a population of counters of which 60% had the number 0 on and 40% had the number 1. The population mean μ was $\frac{2}{5}$ and the population mode was 0 (since 60% of the counters had 0 on them). The two statistics that we calculated were the sample mean $\bar{X}$ and the sample mode M. We could use either of them as estimators for μ, the population mean, but we saw that $E(\bar{X}) = \mu$ but $E(M) \neq \mu$ so we would prefer to use the sample mean $\bar{X}$ rather than the sample mode M as an estimator for μ in this case. How about an estimator for the population mode? Neither of the statistics that we calculated has the property of being unbiased since $E(\bar{X}) = \mu = \frac{2}{5}$ and $E(M) = \frac{44}{125}$, whereas the population mode was 0. Intuitively you might prefer the estimator M since it is, after all, a mode and is also slightly closer to the population mode. In this case we refer to M as a **biased estimator** for the population mode. The **bias** is simply the expected value of the estimator minus the parameter of the population it is estimating.

- **If a statistic T is used as an estimator for a population parameter θ then the**

$$\textbf{bias} = E(T) - \theta$$

In this case the bias is $\frac{44}{125}$.

Returning to the estimation of μ, a little thought will show that $E(X_i) = \mu$ for every value of i. So why should you bother to calculate the mean $\bar{X}$ when *any* member of the sample has the same property: that it provides an unbiased estimator for the mean μ? To answer this question we shall look at some other properties of the estimator $\bar{X}$.

In the general case you have a random sample of size n given by $X_1, X_2, X_3, \ldots X_n$ and each of the X_i have the same distribution as the population so $\mathrm{E}(X_i) = \mu$ and $\mathrm{Var}(X_i) = \sigma^2$. In chapter 6 of Book T1 some important properties of expected values and variances were given:

$$\mathrm{E}(aX) = a\mathrm{E}(X) \quad (1)$$

$$\mathrm{E}(X+Y) = \mathrm{E}(X) + \mathrm{E}(Y) \quad (2)$$

$$\mathrm{Var}(aX) = a^2\mathrm{Var}(X) \quad (3)$$

$$\mathrm{Var}(X+Y) = \mathrm{Var}(X) + \mathrm{Var}(Y) \quad \text{if } X \text{ and } Y \text{ are independent} \quad (4)$$

Now $$\bar{X} = \frac{1}{n}(X_1 + \ldots + X_n)$$

So: $$\mathrm{E}(\bar{X}) = \frac{1}{n}\mathrm{E}(X_1 + \ldots + X_n) \quad \text{by (1)}$$

$$= \frac{1}{n}[\mathrm{E}(X_1) + \ldots + \mathrm{E}(X_n)] \quad \text{by (2)}$$

$$= \frac{1}{n}[\mu + \ldots + \mu]$$

$$= \frac{n\mu}{n}$$

That is: $$\mathrm{E}(\bar{X}) = \mu$$

You can also find $$\mathrm{Var}(\bar{X}) = \frac{1}{n^2}\mathrm{Var}(X_1 + \ldots + X_n) \quad \text{by (3)}$$

$$= \frac{1}{n^2}[\mathrm{Var}(X_1) + \ldots + \mathrm{Var}(X_n)] \quad \text{by (4)}$$

$$= \frac{1}{n^2}[\sigma^2 + \ldots + \sigma^2]$$

$$= \frac{n\sigma^2}{n^2}$$

That is: $$\mathrm{Var}(\bar{X}) = \frac{\sigma^2}{n}$$

Notice that $\bar{X}$ is always an unbiased estimator of μ but also that as the sample size n increases the variance of this estimator *decreases*. It is this property of $\mathrm{Var}(\bar{X})$ that makes $\bar{X}$ a useful estimator of μ and certainly a better estimator than X_1, or any other single member of the sample, since a smaller variance means that the values of any estimates should be closer to the required value μ.

The variance of an estimator is clearly a helpful guide to how useful a particular estimate may be. In calculations you often want to find the standard deviation of the estimator, and this is referred to as the **standard error** of the estimator. So if the estimator is the mean $\bar{X}$ then the standard error of the mean is $\frac{\sigma}{\sqrt{n}}$.

The other population parameter that we are usually interested in is σ^2. You may already have come across the statistic

$$S^2 = \frac{1}{n-1}\Sigma(X-\bar{X})^2 = \frac{1}{n-1}(\Sigma X^2 - n\bar{X}^2)$$

In order to find $\mathrm{E}(S^2)$ you need to recall certain facts about expected values and variances. These are, first:

$$\sigma^2 = \mathrm{Var}(X) = \mathrm{E}(X^2) - \mu^2$$

so: $$\mathrm{E}(X^2) = \sigma^2 + \mu^2 \qquad (5)$$

and, second: $$\mathrm{Var}(\bar{X}) = \frac{\sigma^2}{n} \quad \text{and} \quad \mathrm{E}(\bar{X}) = \mu$$

so: $$\frac{\sigma^2}{n} = \mathrm{E}(\bar{X}^2) - \mu^2$$

and $$\mathrm{E}(\bar{X}^2) = \frac{\sigma^2}{n} + \mu^2 \qquad (6)$$

So if $$S^2 = \frac{1}{n-1}(\Sigma X^2 - n\bar{X}^2)$$

then $$\mathrm{E}(S^2) = \frac{1}{n-1}\mathrm{E}(\Sigma X^2 - n\bar{X}^2)$$

$$= \frac{1}{n-1}[\mathrm{E}(\Sigma X^2) - n\mathrm{E}(\bar{X}^2)]$$

But $\mathrm{E}(\Sigma X^2) = \Sigma\mathrm{E}(X^2) = n\mathrm{E}(X^2)$

so: $$\mathrm{E}(S^2) = \frac{n}{n-1}[\mathrm{E}(X^2) - \mathrm{E}(\bar{X}^2)]$$

$$= \frac{n}{n-1}\left[\sigma^2 + \mu^2 - \left(\frac{\sigma^2}{n} + \mu^2\right)\right] \quad \text{by (5) and (6)}$$

$$= \frac{n}{n-1}\left[\frac{(n-1)}{n}\sigma^2\right]$$

That is: $$\mathrm{E}(S^2) = \sigma^2$$

and so S^2 is an unbiased estimator of the population variance σ^2. It is because of this property of S^2 that we use s^2 to estimate σ^2 in calculations where a value of σ^2 is not known. There is a great deal of confusion in textbooks over S^2 and the sample variance. In this text, as in Book T1, we shall use S^2 for the **sample variance**, and

$$s^2 = \frac{1}{n-1}(\Sigma x^2 - n\bar{x}^2)$$

for the value in the case of a specific sample. No use will be made of the statistic $\frac{\Sigma X^2 - n\bar{X}^2}{n}$ which is used in some books to describe sample variance.

This use of S^2 to describe sample variance is common practice amongst many professional statisticians and it means that the formula for the variance of a *population* of size n, namely

$$\text{Var}(X) = \sigma^2 = \frac{\Sigma X^2 - n\mu^2}{n}$$

is not confused with the formula for *sample* variance, namely

$$S^2 = \frac{\Sigma X^2 - n\bar{X}^2}{n-1}$$

It is a common practice amongst statisticians to use s^2 for both the estimator *and* estimate of σ^2. In the above section we have distinguished between S^2 for the estimator and s^2 for the estimate, but when writing these symbols by hand it is sometimes difficult to distinguish between the two, and this may be a reason for the practice. However, it is usually clear from the context whether an estimator or estimate is being referred to.

Sometimes we use the 'hat' notation to indicate that an estimate of a parameter is being used. Thus an estimate of μ would be called $\hat{\mu}$, so we often have $\bar{x} = \hat{\mu}$, and an estimate of σ^2 would be $\hat{\sigma}^2$, so we might write $s^2 = \hat{\sigma}^2$.

Example 3

The table below summarises the number of breakdowns, x, on a town's bypass on 30 randomly chosen days.

Number of breakdowns	2	3	4	5	6	7	8	9
Number of days	3	5	4	3	5	4	4	2

(a) Calculate unbiased estimates of the mean and variance of the number of breakdowns.

Twenty more days were randomly sampled and this sample had a mean of 6.0 days and $s^2 = 5.0$.

(b) Treating the 50 results as a single sample, obtain further unbiased estimates of the population mean and variance.

(c) Estimate the size of sample required to achieve a standard error of less than 0.25.

(a) By calculator: $\Sigma x = 160$ and $\Sigma x^2 = 990$

So $$\hat{\mu} = \bar{x} = \frac{160}{30} = 5.33$$

and $$\hat{\sigma}^2 = s_x^2 = \frac{990 - 30\bar{x}^2}{29} = 4.7126 = 4.71 \text{ (3 s.f.)}$$

(b) New sample: $\bar{y} = 6.0 \Rightarrow \Sigma y = 20 \times 6.0 = 120$

$$s_y^2 = 5.0 \Rightarrow \frac{\Sigma y^2 - 20 \times 6^2}{19} = 5$$

So: $$\Sigma y^2 = 5 \times 19 + 20 \times 6^2$$

i.e. $$\Sigma y^2 = 815$$

So the combined sample (z) of size 50 has

$$\Sigma z = 160 + 120 = 280$$

$$\Sigma z^2 = 990 + 815 = 1805$$

Then the combined estimate of μ is

$$\bar{z} = \frac{280}{50} = 5.6$$

and the estimate for σ^2 is

$$s_z^2 = \frac{1805 - 50 \times 5.6^2}{49}$$

i.e. $$s_z^2 = 4.8367\ldots = 4.84 \text{ (3 s.f.)}$$

(c) The best estimate of σ^2 will be s_z^2 since it is based on a larger sample than s_x^2 or s_y^2.

So the standard error is $\frac{s_z}{\sqrt{n}} = \sqrt{\frac{4.8367\ldots}{n}}$

To achieve a standard error < 0.25 you require

$$\sqrt{\frac{4.8367\ldots}{n}} < 0.25$$

that is: $$\sqrt{n} > \frac{\sqrt{4.8367\ldots}}{0.25}$$

$$\sqrt{n} > 8.797\ldots$$

$$n > 77.38\ldots$$

So we need a sample of at least 78.

Notice that in example 3 you required the standard error of the mean but did not know σ. Since, in practice, one so often has to use s^2 instead of σ^2 the standard error of the mean is used to refer to either $\frac{\sigma}{\sqrt{n}}$ or $\frac{s}{\sqrt{n}}$ if σ is not known.

- **Standard error of the mean is $\frac{\sigma}{\sqrt{n}}$ or $\frac{s}{\sqrt{n}}$.**

Exercise 2B

1 Find unbiased estimates of the mean and variance of the populations from which the following random samples have been taken:

(a) 21.3; 19.6; 18.5; 22.3; 17.4; 16.3; 18.9; 17.6; 18.7; 16.5; 19.3; 21.8; 20.1; 22.0

(b) 1; 2; 5; 1; 6; 4; 1; 3; 2; 8; 5; 6; 2; 4; 3; 1

(c) 120.4; 230.6; 356.1; 129.8; 185.6; 147.6; 258.3; 329.7; 249.3

(d) 0.862; 0.754; 0.459; 0.473; 0.493; 0.681; 0.743; 0.469; 0.538; 0.361.

2 Find the standard error of the mean for each of the samples in question 1.

3 Find unbiased estimates of the mean and the variance of the populations from which random samples with the following summaries have been taken.

(a) $n = 120$ $\quad \Sigma x = 4368$ $\quad \Sigma x^2 = 162\,466$

(b) $n = 30$ $\quad \Sigma x = 270$ $\quad \Sigma x^2 = 2546$

(c) $n = 1037$ $\quad \Sigma x = 1140.7$ $\quad \Sigma x^2 = 1278.08$

(d) $n = 15$ $\quad \Sigma x = 168$ $\quad \Sigma x^2 = 1913$

4 Find the standard error of the mean for each of the samples in question 3.

5 John and Mary each independently took a random sample of sixth-formers in their college and asked them how much money, in pounds, they earned last week. John used his sample of size 20 to obtain unbiased estimates of the mean and variance of the amount earned by a sixth former at their college last week. He obtained values of $\bar{x} = 15.5$ and $s_x^2 = 8.0$. Mary's sample of size 30 can be summarised as $\Sigma y = 486$ and $\Sigma y^2 = 8222$.

(a) Use Mary's sample to find unbiased estimates of μ and σ^2.

(b) Combine the samples and use all 50 observations to obtain further unbiased estimates of μ and σ^2.

(c) Find the standard error of the mean for each of these estimates of μ.

(d) Comment on which estimate of μ you would prefer to use.

6 A machine operator checks a random sample of 20 bottles off a production line in order to estimate the mean volume of bottles (in cm^3) from this production run. The 20 values can be summarised as $\Sigma x = 1300$ and $\Sigma x^2 = 84\,685$.

(a) Use this sample to find unbiased estimates of μ and σ^2.

A supervisor knows from experience that the standard deviation of volumes on this process, σ, should be $3\,\text{cm}^3$ and he wishes to have an estimate of μ that has a standard error of less than $0.5\,\text{cm}^3$.

(b) What size sample will he need to achieve this?

The supervisor takes a further sample of size 16 and finds $\Sigma x = 1060$.

(c) Combine the two samples to obtain a revised estimate of μ.

7 The heights of certain seedlings after growing for 10 weeks in a greenhouse have a standard deviation of 2.6 cm. Find the smallest sample that must be taken for the standard error of the mean to be less than 0.5 cm.

8 The hardness of a plastic compound was determined by measuring the indentation produced by a heavy pointed device. The following observations in tenths of a millimetre were obtained: 4.7, 5.2, 5.4, 4.8, 4.5, 4.9, 4.5, 5.1, 5.0, 4.8.

(a) Estimate the mean indentation for this compound.

(b) Estimate the size of sample required in order that in future the standard error of the mean should be just less than 0.05.

9 Prospective army recruits receive a medical test. The probability of each recruit passing the test is p, independent of any other recruit. The medicals are carried out over two days and on the first day n recruits are seen and on the next day $2n$ are seen. Let X_1 be the number of recruits who pass the test on the first day and let X_2 be the number who pass on the second day.

(a) Write down $\text{E}(X_1)$, $\text{E}(X_2)$, $\text{Var}(X_1)$ and $\text{Var}(X_2)$.

(b) Show that $\dfrac{X_1}{n}$ and $\dfrac{X_2}{2n}$ are both unbiased estimates of p and state, giving a reason, which you would prefer to use.

(c) Show that $X = \frac{1}{2}\left(\frac{X_1}{n} + \frac{X_2}{2n}\right)$ is an unbiased estimator of p.

(d) Show that $Y = \left(\frac{X_1 + X_2}{3n}\right)$ is an unbiased estimator of p.

(e) Which of the statistics X_1, X_2, X or Y is the best estimator of p?

The statistic $T = \left(\frac{2X_1 + X_2}{3n}\right)$ is proposed as an estimator of p.

(f) Find the bias.

10 Two independent random samples $X_1, X_2, \ldots X_n$ and $Y_1, Y_2, \ldots Y_m$ are taken from a population with mean μ and variance σ^2. The unbiased estimators $\bar{X}$ and $\bar{Y}$ of μ are calculated. A new unbiased estimator T of μ is sought of the form $T = r\bar{X} + s\bar{Y}$.

(a) Show that since T is unbiased then $r + s = 1$.

(b) By writing $T = r\bar{X} + (1 - r)\bar{Y}$, show that

$$\mathrm{Var}(T) = \sigma^2\left[\frac{r^2}{n} + \frac{(1-r)^2}{m}\right]$$

(c) Show that the minimum variance of T is when $r = \frac{n}{n+m}$.

(d) Find the best (in the sense of minimum variance) estimator of μ of the form $r\bar{X} + s\bar{Y}$.

11 A random variable X has a continuous uniform distribution over the interval $[0, \alpha]$. A random sample of size n is taken of observations of X.

(a) Find $\mathrm{E}(\bar{X})$.

(b) Suggest an unbiased estimator of α.

(c) Find the standard error of your estimator.

12 An electrical company repairs very large numbers of television sets and wishes to estimate the mean time taken to repair a particular fault.

It is known from previous research that the standard deviation of the time taken to repair this particular fault is 2.5 minutes. The manager wishes to ensure that the probability that the estimate differs from the true mean by less than 30 seconds is 0.95. Find how large a sample is required. [L]

13 The concentrations, in mg per litre, of a trace element in 7 randomly chosen samples of water from a spring were:

240.8 237.3 236.7 236.6 234.2 233.9 232.5.

Determine unbiased estimates of the mean and the variance of the concentration of the trace element per litre of water from the spring. [L]

14 Cartons of orange are filled by a machine. A sample of 10 cartons selected at random from the production contained the following quantities of orange (in ml).

201.2 205.0 209.1 202.3 204.6
206.4 210.1 201.9 203.7 207.3

Calculate unbiased estimates of the mean and variance of the population from which this sample was taken. [L]

2.3 The central limit theorem

So far you have seen how you can find an estimate for μ, the population mean. Suppose that a random sample of 50 students from a sixth form college had an average height of 1.73 m; then you would write $\bar{x} = 1.73$ and say that your estimate of μ was 1.73. In practical terms, though, this single value may not be useful as you do not know how accurate your estimate is. The next stage in the estimation process is to give an *interval* or *range of values* (1.73 $\pm$ something) for your estimate of μ and to be able to attach a measure of accuracy or **confidence** to the range of values you have given. Before you can do this, however, you need to know something about the **distribution of the sample mean $\bar{X}$.**

Earlier in this chapter (page 13) we saw that if the random sample was taken from a population that was distributed normally with mean μ and variance σ^2 then ΣX will have a $\mathrm{N}(n\mu, n\sigma^2)$ distribution. It is a short step to see that in this case $\bar{X} \sim \mathrm{N}\left(\mu, \dfrac{\sigma^2}{n}\right)$. But what will the distribution of $\bar{X}$ be when the population from which the sample was taken does *not* have a normal distribution? The answer in general is that it depends upon the distribution of the population and in most cases there is no easy way of describing the distribution of $\bar{X}$. However, there is an important result that enables you to say something about the distribution of $\bar{X}$ when the sample size n is large. This result is known as the **central limit theorem** and it tells you that when n is large $\bar{X}$ is approximately normally distributed, whether or not the *population* is normally distributed.

- **The central limit theorem says that if $X_1, X_2, \ldots X_n$ is a random sample of size n from a population with mean μ and variance σ^2 then**

$$\bar{X} \text{ is approximately } \sim \mathrm{N}\left(\mu, \frac{\sigma^2}{n}\right)$$

This theorem is of fundamental importance in the theory of statistics and is one of the main reasons why the normal distribution is so useful. The theorem is an approximation but the approximation improves as n, the sample size, increases; this is another reason (remember $\mathrm{Var}(\bar{X})$ gets smaller as n increases) why a large sample is often desirable.

A proof of this theorem is beyond the scope of this course, but with a little thought you should be able to see why it might be true. Consider a table of random digits from 0 to 9. Since the digits are random each digit has the same probability of being chosen, namely $\frac{1}{10}$, and the mean, μ, of the population of random digits is $4.5(0 \times \frac{1}{10} + 1 \times \frac{1}{10} + \ldots + 9 \times \frac{1}{10})$. Now imagine taking a sample of ten random digits and calculating the mean $\bar{x}$. If you use the first row of Table 7 (p. 210) you would obtain:

$$8, 6, 1, 3, 8, 4, 1, 0, 0, 7$$

So:

$$\bar{x} = \frac{38}{10}$$

$$= 3.8$$

Notice that our sample has some high (e.g. 8) and some low (e.g. 0) digits but the high and low values tend to cancel each other out so that the mean value for the sample is close to the mean for the population as a whole. It is therefore much more unlikely that you would get a mean $\bar{x}$ of 0 or 8 than a value close to μ. It is this 'cancelling out' effect of taking a mean that might lead you to expect the distribution of $\bar{X}$ to peak close to μ and tail off at each end. It is a worthwhile experiment to repeat this sampling of random numbers and obtain a large number of observations of $\bar{X}$. A histogram of these $\bar{x}$ values can be plotted and a shape approximating to a normal distribution should result.

Example 4

A sample of size 9 is taken from a population with distribution $N(10, 2^2)$. Find the probability that the sample mean $\bar{X}$ is more than 11.

The population is normal, so $\bar{X}$ will have a normal distribution despite the small size of the sample. The variance of $\bar{X}$ is $\frac{\sigma^2}{n}$ so in this case

$$\text{Var}(\bar{X}) = \frac{\sigma^2}{n} = \frac{2^2}{9} = (\tfrac{2}{3})^2$$

So: $$\bar{X} \sim N(10, (\tfrac{2}{3})^2)$$

In Book T1 you saw that if a random variable $Y \sim N(\mu, \sigma^2)$ then you could find probabilities for Y by transforming to the standard normal Z and using tables (see Table 3, p. 207) where

$$Z = \frac{Y - \mu}{\sigma}$$

In this case the mean of $\bar{X}$ is 10 and the standard deviation is $\frac{2}{3}$, so:

$$\begin{aligned} P(\bar{X} > 11) &= P\left(Z > \frac{11 - 10}{\frac{2}{3}}\right) \\ &= P(Z > 1.5) \\ &= 1 - 0.9332 \\ &= 0.0668 \end{aligned}$$

Example 5

A cubical die is relabelled so that there are three faces marked 1, two faces marked 3 and one marked 6. The die is rolled 40 times and the mean of the 40 scores is recorded. Find an approximation for the probability that the mean is over 3.

Let the random variable X = the score on a single roll; then the distribution of X is

X:	1	3	6
p(x):	$\frac{1}{2}$	$\frac{1}{3}$	$\frac{1}{6}$

So: $$\begin{aligned} \mu = E(X) &= 1 \times \tfrac{1}{2} + 3 \times \tfrac{1}{3} + 6 \times \tfrac{1}{6} \\ &= 2.5 \end{aligned}$$

and $$\begin{aligned} \sigma^2 = \text{Var}(X) &= 1^2 \times \tfrac{1}{2} + 3^2 \times \tfrac{1}{3} + 6^2 \times \tfrac{1}{6} - (\tfrac{5}{2})^2 \\ &= \tfrac{19}{2} - \tfrac{25}{4} \\ &= 3.25 \text{ or } \tfrac{13}{4} \end{aligned}$$

Now by the central limit theorem $\bar{X} \approx\sim N(2.5, \frac{13}{160})$

So: $$\mathrm{P}(\bar{X} > 3) = \mathrm{P}\left(Z > \frac{3 - 2.5}{\sqrt{\frac{13}{160}}}\right)$$
$$= \mathrm{P}(Z > 1.75)$$
$$= 1 - 0.9599$$
$$= 0.0401 \text{ or } 0.040 \text{ (3 d.p.)}$$

It is worth pointing out that although the X_i and therefore $\bar{X}$ are discrete distributions, whereas the normal distribution is a continuous distribution, a continuity correction is not appropriate in this example. However, if you had been asked to find a probability for ΣX such as $\mathrm{P}(\Sigma X > 120)$, then a continuity correction as described in Book T1 (chapter 8) could be applied. The continuity correction described in Book T1 can only be applied to random variables that take *integer* values so it could be applied to ΣX in this instance but not $\bar{X}$.

First notice that, as a result of the central limit theorem, the distribution of ΣX is approximately normal.

Also: $$\mathrm{E}(\Sigma X) = 40 \times \mathrm{E}(X) = 40 \times 2.5 = 100$$

and $$\mathrm{Var}(\Sigma X) = 40 \times \mathrm{Var}(X) = 40 \times \tfrac{13}{4} = 130$$

So: $$\Sigma X \sim \mathrm{N}(100, (\sqrt{130})^2)$$

and $$\mathrm{P}(\Sigma X > 120) = \mathrm{P}\left(Z > \frac{120.5 - 100}{\sqrt{130}}\right)$$
$$= \mathrm{P}(Z > 1.80)$$
$$= 1 - 0.9641$$
$$= 0.04 \text{ (2 d.p.)}$$

Exercise 2C

1 A sample of size 6 is taken from a normal distribution $\mathrm{N}(10, 2^2)$. What is the probability that the sample mean exceeds 12?

2 A machine fills cartons in such a way that the amount of drink in each carton is distributed normally with a mean of $40\,\mathrm{cm}^3$ and a standard deviation of $1.5\,\mathrm{cm}^3$.

(a) A sample of four cartons is examined. Find the probability that the mean amount of drink is more than $40.5\,\mathrm{cm}^3$.

(b) A sample of 49 cartons is examined. Find the probability that the mean amount of drink is more than $40.5\,\text{cm}^3$ on this occasion.

3 The lengths of bolts produced by a machine have an unknown distribution with mean 3.03 cm and standard deviation 0.20 cm. A sample of 100 bolts is taken.

(a) Find the probability that the mean length of this sample is less than 3 cm.

(b) What size sample is required if the probability that the mean is less than 3 cm is to be less than 1%?

4 Forty observations are taken from a population with distribution given by the probability density function

$$f(x) = \begin{cases} \frac{2}{9}x, & 0 \leqslant x \leqslant 3 \\ 0, & \text{otherwise} \end{cases}$$

(a) Find the mean and variance of this population.

(b) Find the probability that the mean of the 40 observations is more than 2.10.

5 A fair die is rolled 35 times.

(a) Find the approximate probability that the mean of the 35 scores is more than 4.

(b) Find the approximate probability that the total of the 35 scores is less than 100.

6 The 25 children in a class each roll a fair die 30 times and record the number of sixes they obtain. Find the probability that the mean number of sixes recorded for the class is less than 4.5.

7 The error in mm made in measuring the length of a table has a uniform distribution over the range $[-5, 5]$. The table is measured 20 times. Find the probability that the mean error is less than -1 mm.

8 Telephone calls arrive at an exchange at an average rate of two per minute. Over a period of 30 days a telephonist records the number of calls that arrive in the five-minute period before her break.

(a) Find an approximation for the probability that the total number of calls recorded is more than 350.

(b) Estimate the probability that the mean number of calls is less than 9.0.

9 How many times must a fair die be rolled in order for there to be a less than 1% chance that the mean of all the scores differs from 3.5 by more than 0.1?

10 The heights of women in a certain area have a mean of 175 cm and a standard deviation of 2.5 cm. The heights of men in the same area have a mean of 177 cm and a standard deviation of 2.0 cm. Samples of 40 women and 50 men are taken and their heights are recorded. Find the probability that the mean of the men is more than 3 cm greater than the mean of the women.

11 A computer, in adding numbers, rounds each number off to the nearest integer. All the rounding errors are independent and come from a uniform distribution over the range $[-0.5, 0.5]$.

(a) Given that 1000 numbers are added find the probability that the total error is greater than $+10$.

(b) Find how many numbers can be added together so that the probability that the magnitude of the total error is less than 10 is at least 0.95.

2.4 Confidence intervals

You are now in a position to complete the estimation of μ, the population mean. In the previous sections we considered taking a random sample of 50 students from a sixth form college and measuring their heights. Now we shall assume that the standard deviation of heights of students in the sixth form college, i.e. σ, is known to be 3.5 cm but the mean μ (in metres) is *not* known and this is the parameter we seek to estimate. Suppose the sample gave an estimate $\bar{x} = 1.73$. What can you say about μ?

You know that an estimate of μ is $\hat{\mu} = 1.73$, but it would be more helpful if you could give a range of values for μ and also provide some measure of how reliable this range of values is. People sometimes use phrases like 'I'm 90% (or 99% or 95%) certain that I left the keys on the kitchen table'. In statistics we use the properties of the standard normal distribution, $N(0, 1^2)$, to formalise this idea and arrive at a range of values for μ about which we are, say, 95% confident.

You know that, whatever the distribution of heights in the population, by the central limit theorem

$$\bar{X} \text{ is approximately} \sim N\left(\mu, \frac{3.5^2}{50}\right)$$

and therefore

$$Z = \frac{\bar{X} - \mu}{\frac{3.5}{\sqrt{50}}} \sim \mathrm{N}(0, 1^2)$$

Using Table 4 you can see that for the $\mathrm{N}(0, 1^2)$ distribution

$$\mathrm{P}(Z > 1.9600) = \mathrm{P}(Z < -1.9600) = 0.025$$

and so 95% of the distribution is between -1.9600 and 1.9600.

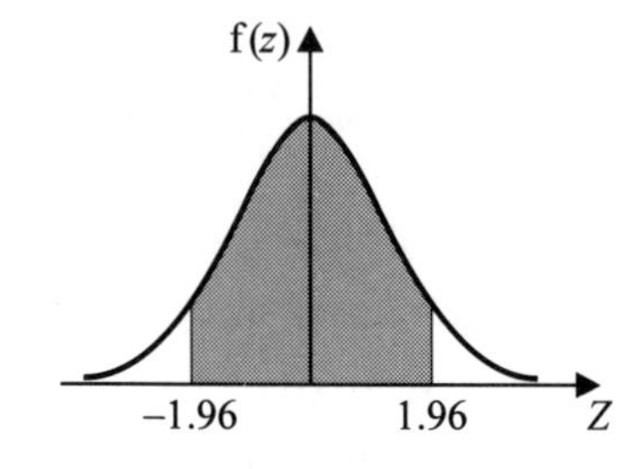

So $$\mathrm{P}(-1.96 < Z < 1.96) = 0.95$$

i.e. $$\mathrm{P}\left(-1.96 < \frac{\bar{X} - \mu}{\frac{3.5}{\sqrt{50}}} < 1.96\right) = 0.95$$

Look at the inequality inside the probability statement:

$$-1.96 \times \frac{3.5}{\sqrt{50}} < \bar{X} - \mu < 1.96 \times \frac{3.5}{\sqrt{50}}$$

and start to isolate μ:

$$-1.96 \times \frac{3.5}{\sqrt{50}} - \bar{X} < -\mu < 1.96 \times \frac{3.5}{\sqrt{50}} - \bar{X}$$

Multiply by -1 and change the inequality:

$$\bar{X} + 1.96 \times \frac{3.5}{\sqrt{50}} > \mu > \bar{X} - 1.96 \times \frac{3.5}{\sqrt{50}}$$

If you use the specific estimate of $\bar{x} = 173$ (in cm), you get

$$173 + 1.96 \times \frac{3.5}{\sqrt{50}} > \mu > 173 - 1.96 \times \frac{3.5}{\sqrt{50}}$$

or $$174.0 > \mu > 172.0$$

We say that a **95% confidence interval** for μ is (172.0, 174.0). This enables us to say a little more about our estimate of μ: μ should lie between 172.0 and 174.0. The upper and lower values of a confidence interval are sometimes called the **confidence limits**.

In general we have the following formula:

- **The 95% confidence interval for μ is**

$$\bar{x} \pm 1.96 \times \frac{\sigma}{\sqrt{n}}$$

What exactly is a confidence interval and how should it be interpreted?

First, it is important to remember that μ is a fixed, but unknown, number and as such it cannot vary and does *not* have a *distribution* so it does not make sense to talk about the probability that μ is between certain values. Secondly, it *is* worth remembering that we base a 95% confidence interval on a probability statement about the normal distribution $Z \sim N(0, 1^2)$. The choice of 95% gave rise to z values of ± 1.96 and, as you can see from Table 4, a 90% confidence interval would use z values of ± 1.6449 instead of ± 1.96 since $P(Z > 1.6449) = P(Z < -1.6449) = 0.05$. However, although you start by considering probabilities associated with the random variable Z, the final confidence interval does *not* tell you that the probability that μ lies inside the interval is 0.95. Rather, since μ is fixed, it is the *confidence interval* that varies (according to the value of $\bar{x}$). What a 95% confidence interval tells you is that the probability that the interval contains μ is 0.95. The following diagram illustrates the 95% confidence intervals calculated from different samples and also shows the position of μ.

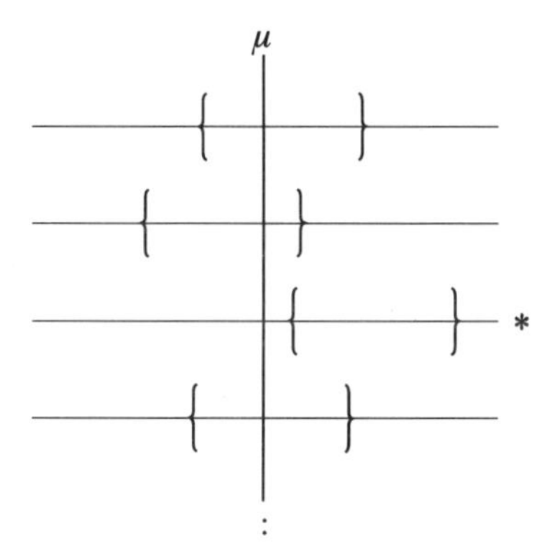

Suppose 50 samples of size 100 were taken and 95% confidence intervals for μ were calculated for each sample. This would give 50 different confidence intervals each based on one of the 50 different values of $\bar{x}$. If you imagine for a moment that you actually do know what the value of μ is then you can plot each of these confidence intervals on a diagram similar to the one here: you would expect that 95% of these confidence intervals would contain the value μ but about once in every 20 times you would get an interval which did not contain μ (like the one marked * here). The problem for the statistician is that he or she never knows whether the confidence interval they have just calculated is one that contains μ or not. However, they can rest assured that 95% (or 90% or 99% depending on the degree of confidence required) of the time they will be right! The choice of what level of confidence to use in a particular situation will depend on the problem involved but a value of 95% is commonly used if no other value is specified.

Example 6

The breaking strains of reels of string produced at a certain factory have a standard deviation of 1.5 kg. A sample of 100 reels from a certain batch were tested and their mean breaking strain was 5.30 kg.

(a) Find a 95% confidence interval for the mean breaking strain of string in this batch.

The manufacturer becomes concerned if the lower 95% confidence limit falls below 5 kg. A sample of 80 reels from another batch gave a mean breaking strain of 5.31 kg.

(b) Will the manufacturer be concerned?

The distribution for breaking strains is not known but the sample is quite large and by the central limit theorem $\bar{X}$ will be approximately normally distributed so

(a) 95% confidence interval (C.I.) is

$$\bar{x} \pm 1.96 \times \frac{\sigma}{\sqrt{n}} = 5.30 \pm 1.96 \times \frac{1.5}{\sqrt{100}}$$
$$= (5.006, 5.594)$$

(b) Lower 95% confidence limit is

$$\bar{x} - 1.96 \times \frac{\sigma}{\sqrt{n}} = 5.31 - \frac{1.96 \times 1.5}{\sqrt{80}}$$
$$= 4.98$$

so the manufacturer will be concerned.

We are sometimes interested in the **width** of a confidence interval, which is simply defined as the difference between the upper confidence limit and the lower confidence limit. There are three factors that affect the width: the value of σ, the size of the sample n and the degree of confidence required. In a particular example where σ and n are determined the only factor you can change to alter the width is the degree of confidence. A high level of confidence (e.g. 99%) will give a greater width than a lower level of confidence (e.g. 90%) and the statistician has to weigh up the advantages of high confidence against greater width when calculating a confidence interval.

Example 7

A random sample of size 25 is taken from a normal population with standard deviation of 2.5. The mean of the sample was 17.8.

(a) Find a 99% C.I. for the population mean μ.

(b) What size sample is required to obtain a 99% C.I. of width at most 1.5?

(c) What confidence level would be associated with the interval based on the above sample of 25 but of width 1.5, i.e. (17.05, 18.55)?

Using Table 4 on page 208,

(a) 99% C.I. is

$$\bar{x} \pm 2.5758 \times \frac{\sigma}{\sqrt{n}} = 17.8 \pm 2.5758 \times \frac{2.5}{\sqrt{25}}$$
$$= (16.51, 19.09)$$

(b) Width of 99% C.I. is $\quad 2 \times 2.5758 \times \dfrac{2.5}{\sqrt{n}}$

so you require $\quad 1.5 > \dfrac{12.879\ldots}{\sqrt{n}}$

i.e. $\quad n > 73.719\ldots$

so you need $\quad n = 74$

(c) A width of 1.5 $\Rightarrow$ $\quad 1.5 = 2 \times z \times \dfrac{2.5}{\sqrt{25}}$

$$z = 1.5$$

From Table 4 you find that

$$P(Z < 1.5) = 0.9332$$

and so $\quad P(Z > 1.5) = P(Z < -1.5) = 1 - 0.9332$
$$= 0.0668$$

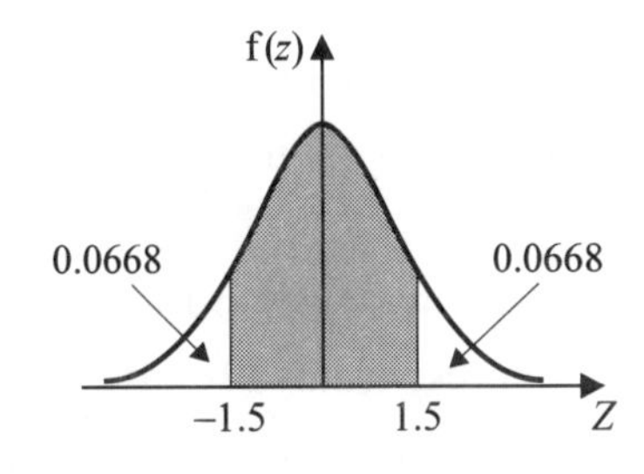

So the confidence level is $100 \times (1 - 2 \times 0.0668) = 86.6\%$.

Exercise 2D

1 A sample of size 9 is taken from a normal distribution with variance 36. The sample mean is 128.

(a) Find a 95% confidence interval for the mean μ of the distribution.

(b) Find a 99% confidence interval for the mean μ of the distribution.

2 A sample of size 25 is taken from a normal distribution with standard deviation 4. The sample mean is 85.

(a) Find a 90% confidence interval for the mean μ of the distribution.

(b) Find a 95% confidence interval for the mean μ of the distribution.

3 A normal distribution has mean μ and variance 4.41. A random sample has the following values:

$$23.1, \quad 21.8, \quad 24.6, \quad 22.5$$

Use this sample to find 98% confidence limits for the mean μ.

4 A normal distribution has standard deviation 15. Estimate the sample size required if the following confidence intervals for the mean should have width of less than 2.

(a) 90% (b) 95% (c) 99%

5 Repeat question 4 for a normal distribution with standard deviation 2.4 and a desired width of less than 0.8.

6 An experienced poultry farmer knows that the mean weight μ kg for a large population of chickens will vary from season to season but the standard deviation of the weights should remain at 0.70 kg. A random sample of 100 chickens is taken from the population and the weight x kg of each chicken in the sample is recorded giving $\Sigma x = 190.2$. Find a 95% confidence interval for μ.

7 A railway watchdog is studying the number of seconds that express trains are late in arriving. Previous surveys of this nature have shown that the standard deviation is 50. A random sample of 200 trains was selected and gave rise to a mean of 310 seconds late. Find a 90% confidence interval for the mean number of seconds that express trains are late.

8 An investigation was carried out into the total distance travelled by lorries in current use. The standard deviation can be assumed to be 15 000 km. A sample of 80 lorries were stopped and their mean distance travelled was found to be 75 872 km. Find a 90% confidence interval for the mean distance travelled by lorries in current use.

9 It is known that each year the standard deviation of the marks in a certain examination is 13.5 but the mean mark μ will fluctuate. An examiner wishes to estimate the mean mark of all the candidates on the examination but he only has the marks of a sample of 250 candidates which give a sample mean of 68.4.

(a) What assumption about these candidates must the examiner make in order to use this sample mean to calculate a confidence interval for μ?

(b) Assuming that the above assumption is justified, calculate a 95% confidence interval for μ.

Later the examiner discovers that the actual value of μ was 65.3.

(c) What conclusions might the examiner draw about his sample?

10 The number of hours for which an electronic device can retain information has a uniform distribution over the range $[\mu - 10, \mu + 10]$ but the value of μ is not known.

(a) Show that the variance of the number of hours the device can retain the information for is $\frac{100}{3}$.

A random sample of 120 devices are tested and the mean number of hours they retained information for was 78.7.

(b) Find a 95% confidence interval for μ.

11 A statistics student calculated a 95% and a 99% confidence interval for the mean μ of a certain population but failed to label them. The two intervals were

$$(22.7, 27.3) \quad \text{and} \quad (23.2, 26.8)$$

(a) State, with a reason, which interval is the 95% one.

(b) Estimate the standard error of the mean in this case.

(c) What was the student's unbiased estimate of the mean μ in this case?

12 A 95% confidence interval for a mean μ is 85.3 ± 2.35. Find the following confidence intervals for μ.

(a) 90% (b) 98% (c) 99%

13 The managing director of a certain firm has commissioned a survey to estimate the mean expenditure of customers on electrical appliances. A random sample of 100 people were questioned and the research team presented the managing director with a 95% confidence interval of (£128.14, £141.86). The director says that this interval is too wide and wants a confidence interval of total width £10.

(a) Using the same value of $\bar{x}$ find the confidence limits in this case.

(b) Find the level of confidence for the interval in part (a).

The managing director is still not happy and now wishes to know how large a sample would be required to obtain a 95% confidence interval of total width no more than £10.

(c) Find the smallest size of sample that will satisfy this request.

14 A plant produces steel sheets whose weights are known to be normally distributed with a standard deviation of 2.4 kg. A random sample of 36 sheets had a mean weight of 31.4 kg. Find 99% confidence limits for the population mean. [L]

15 A machine is regulated to dispense liquid into cartons in such a way that the amount of liquid dispensed on each occasion is normally distributed with a standard deviation of 20 ml.
Find 99% confidence limits for the mean amount of liquid dispensed if a random sample of 40 cartons had an average content of 266 ml. [L]

16 The error made when a certain instrument is used to measure the body length of a butterfly of a particular species is known to be normally distributed with mean 0 and standard deviation 1 mm. Calculate, to 3 decimal places, the probability that the error made when the instrument is used once is numerically less than 0.4 mm.
Given that the body length of a butterfly is measured 9 times with the instrument, calculate, to 3 decimal places, the probability that the mean of the 9 readings will be within 0.5 mm of the true length.
Given that the mean of the 9 readings was 22.53 mm, determine a 98% confidence interval for the true body length of the butterfly. [L]

2.5 What is a hypothesis test?

The scene is a courtroom. The defendant is in the dock and is accused of committing murder. The prosecution and defence counsels will both present evidence and the judge and jury have to reach a verdict. Two important principles operate under the system of British law and they are:

1. the defendant is 'innocent until proved guilty'
2. the proof must be 'beyond all reasonable doubt'.

Clearly the defendant either did or did not commit the murder but, during the course of the trial, the assumption the judge and jury must make is that he did not (i.e. that he is innocent). They must then examine the evidence and essentially answer the following question:

If the defendant is innocent what is the probability of obtaining evidence like this?

If this probability is very small then they will conclude that the assumption of innocence is not sustainable and declare the defendant guilty. For example, if the defendant's fingerprints were found on the gun that shot the victim and the defendant was seen leaving the scene shortly after the time of death then you might think that the probability of these events happening and the defendant being innocent is quite small. Followers of TV detective programmes will know that it may well not be sufficiently small to secure a conviction though!

The above situation is very similar to the processes involved in carrying out a **hypothesis test**. The role of the defendant is played by the **hypotheses**. We start with a basic assumption called the **null hypothesis** (this is equivalent to the defendant being innocent), which is assumed to be true. We also specify the **alternative hypothesis** which describes the situation if the null hypothesis is not true (in the above situation it would be that the defendant was guilty and did commit the murder). In a statistical hypothesis test the evidence comes from a *sample*. This sample is summarised in the form of a statistic called a **test statistic** and by assuming the null hypothesis to be true it should be possible to calculate probabilities relating to this test statistic.

At this point another feature of the courtroom scenario is worth mentioning. Suppose that at the end of the trial the evidence presented is such that the judge and jury could decide that the defendant is guilty. Further evidence detrimental to the defendant could still be produced but a certain *threshold* has already been crossed. The probability of obtaining evidence as bad as this or worse is sufficiently small to cause the judge and jury to reject the defendant's innocence. The phrase **'as bad or worse'** is sometimes helpful. We calculate the probability of obtaining evidence *as bad or worse* as that which we have been presented with to make our judgement.

We said that the judge and jury must assess the evidence and attempt to estimate the probability of obtaining evidence 'as bad or worse' as that presented *if the defendant is innocent*. If that probability is very small they would reject the assumption of innocence, but how small is 'very small'? Clearly there is a *threshold* probability and it may vary, depending on the nature of the problem. In the context of a hypothesis test we call this threshold probability the **significance level**.

- **If the probability of a value of the test statistic 'as bad or worse' as that obtained is p then we reject the null hypothesis if p is less than or equal to the significance level $\alpha\%$.**

The significance level is the level of probability that we call *unlikely*. If your test gives a probability as unlikely as the significance level then you reject the null hypothesis. The usual significance level is 5% or 0.05 but other levels such as 1% (0.01) and 10% (0.10) are often used.

2.6 Hypothesis test for the mean of a normal distribution

A certain company sells fruit juice in cartons. The amount of juice in a carton has a normal distribution with a standard deviation of 3 ml. The company claims that the mean amount of juice per carton, μ, is 60 ml. A trading inspector has received complaints that the company is overstating the mean amount of juice per carton and he wishes to investigate the company's claim. The test that the trading inspector wishes to carry out is about the mean amount of juice per carton, μ, and it is a general feature of hypothesis tests that they are about *the value of unknown population parameters*. The defendant in this case is the company and its stated value for μ. We assume that the company is innocent and wish to formulate a null hypothesis to express this idea in terms of the parameter μ. We usually write H_0 for the null hypothesis and in this case you have:

$$H_0 : \mu = 60$$

If the company is guilty then μ must be less than 60 (in this case we would not be complaining if the cartons contained on average more than 60 ml) and we write the alternative hypothesis H_1 as

$$H_1 : \mu < 60$$

This specification gives you a **one-tailed test**, since you are only considering deviations of μ in one direction, namely $\mu < 60$. If the machine had just been serviced then the company may well be interested in whether μ is *more* than 60 ml (and the machine needs adjusting to stop overfilling the cartons) or *less* than 60 ml (in which case they might be liable to prosecution). In this situation you would specify the alternative hypothesis as

$$H_1 : \mu \neq 60$$

and this is called a **two-tailed test** since you are considering deviations of μ in two directions.

We need some procedure to decide between these two opposing hypotheses and the one that we use is called a **hypothesis test**.

- **A hypothesis test about a population parameter θ tests a null hypothesis H_0, specifying a particular value for θ, against an alternative hypothesis H_1, which will indicate whether the test is one-tailed or two-tailed.**

The trading inspector needed some evidence upon which to base a judgement and he took a random sample of 16 cartons which gave a mean of 59.1 ml. The inspector then had to calculate the probability of obtaining evidence 'as bad or worse' than this, assuming that the null hypothesis is true. What sort of evidence would be 'as bad or worse' than that which the inspector's sample gave? The alternative hypothesis is that the company is deceiving customers and that $\mu < 60$; the inspector's sample gave a mean of 59.1 and so any value of the sample mean *less than or equal to* 59.1 will be 'as bad or worse'.

The situation can be summarised as follows:

1. The random sample $X_1, X_2, \ldots X_{16}$ taken from a population distributed $N(\mu, 3^2)$ has given a sample mean $\bar{x} = 59.1$.
2. If H_0 is true then $\mu = 60$ and all the $X_i \sim N(60, 3^2)$.
3. The inspector wishes to calculate $P(\bar{X} \leqslant 59.1)$.

You know that $\sigma = 3$ so the standard error is $\frac{3}{\sqrt{16}}$ and therefore $\bar{X} \sim N(60, (\frac{3}{4})^2)$.

So:
$$\begin{aligned} P(\bar{X} \leqslant 59.1) &= P\left(Z \leqslant \frac{59.1 - 60}{\frac{3}{4}}\right) \\ &= P(Z \leqslant -1.2) \\ &= 0.1151 \end{aligned}$$

This probability (about 11.5%) is quite large (it is certainly more than 5%, which is the usual significance level) so there is no reason to suspect the validity of H_0 and the company remain innocent. We usually say that the sample is **not significant** and we do not reject the hypothesis that $\mu = 60$.

Notice that the test was based on the statistic

$$Z = \frac{\bar{X} - 60}{\frac{3}{\sqrt{n}}}$$

(recall that a statistic must not contain any unknown population parameters) and this is the **test statistic** in this case.

It is sometimes helpful to consider what value z of the test statistic the inspector would have needed if he were to secure a conviction (or have significant evidence to reject the company's claim that $\mu = 60$). If you use a 5% significance level then (from Table 4 on p. 208):

$$P(Z \leqslant -1.6449) = 0.05$$

so any value of $z \leqslant -1.6449$ would mean that the probability of obtaining a sample 'as bad or worse' is less than or equal to 5%, which is unlikely. This means that the assumption that H_0 is true is called into question and we *reject H_0 at the 5% level of significance.* We call the region $Z \leqslant -1.6449$ the **critical region** of the statistic Z and the value -1.6449 is sometimes called the **critical value.**

- **The critical region of a test statistic T is the range of values of T such that if the value of T, namely t, obtained from your particular sample lies in this critical region then you reject the null hypothesis.**
- **The boundary value(s) of the critical region is (are) called the critical value(s).**

Example 8

At a certain college new students are weighed when they join the college. The distribution of weights of students at the college when they enrol is normal, with a standard deviation of 7.5 kg and a mean of 70 kg. A random sample of 90 students from the new entry were weighed and their mean weight was 71.6 kg. Assuming that the standard deviation has not changed and that the weights of the new class were also normally distributed, test, at the 5% level, whether there is evidence that the mean of the new entry is more than 70 kg.

$H_0 : \mu = 70 \qquad H_1 : \mu > 70$ (so a one-tailed test is required)

$$\sigma = 7.5$$

A 5% significance level is required so the critical region for Z will be as shown by the diagram on the right.

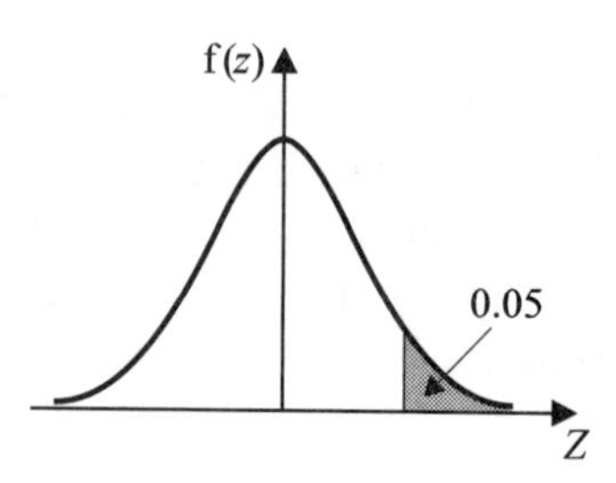

From Table 4 this is $Z \geqslant 1.6449$.

The sample gives $n = 90$, $\bar{x} = 71.6$ and these give a value of the test statistic of

$$z = \frac{71.6 - 70}{\frac{7.5}{\sqrt{90}}} = 2.0239$$

This value *is* in the critical region, so you reject H_0 and conclude that there *is* evidence that the new class have a higher mean weight.

Notice that you could have tackled this example by calculating $P(\bar{X} \geqslant 71.6)$ (the probability of evidence 'as bad or worse') and this would give

$$\begin{aligned} P(\bar{X} \geqslant 71.6) &= P\left(Z \geqslant \frac{71.6 - 70}{\frac{7.5}{\sqrt{90}}}\right) \\ &= P(Z \geqslant 2.02\ldots) \\ &= 1 - 0.9783 \\ &= 0.0217 \end{aligned}$$

You would then argue that this probability of about 2% is very small (since it is less than 5% which was the designated significance level) and therefore the validity of H_0 is called into question and you reject H_0 and conclude that there *is* evidence of an increase in mean.

In practical terms it is often more helpful to know what the critical region for the test statistic $\bar{X}$ is. You can find this by starting from the critical region for Z and in this example

$$Z \geqslant 1.6449$$

So:

$$\frac{\bar{X} - 70}{\frac{7.5}{\sqrt{90}}} \geqslant 1.6449$$

and:

$$\bar{X} \geqslant 1.6449 \times \frac{7.5}{\sqrt{90}} + 70$$

i.e.

$$\bar{X} \geqslant 71.3\ldots$$

so any value of $\bar{x} \geqslant 71.3$ would lead you to reject H_0.

Example 9

A machine produces bolts of diameter D where D has a normal distribution with mean 0.580 cm and standard deviation 0.015 cm. The machine is serviced and after the service a random sample of 50 bolts from the next production run is taken to see if the mean diameter of the bolts has changed from 0.580 cm. The distribution of the diameters of bolts after the service is still normal with a standard deviation of 0.015 cm. The mean diameter of the 50 bolts is 0.577 cm. Test, at the 1% level, whether or not there is evidence that the mean diameter of the bolts has changed.

$H_0 : \mu = 0.580 \qquad H_1 : \mu \neq 0.580$ (so a two-tailed test)

$$\sigma = 0.015$$

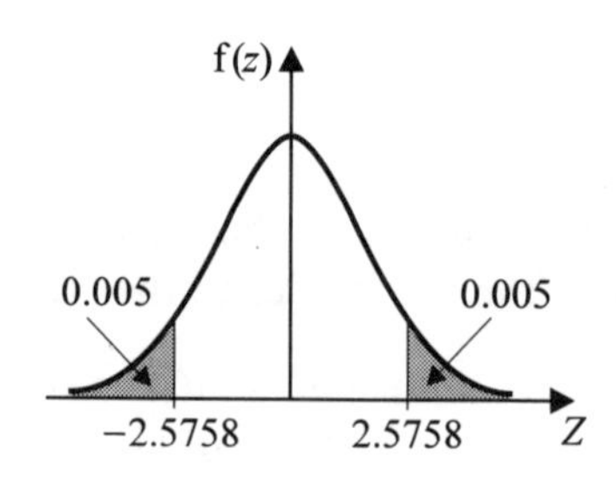

A 1% significance test is required so the critical region for Z will be as shown by the diagram on the right.

From Table 4 the critical region of Z is $Z \leqslant -2.5758$ or $Z \geqslant 2.5758$.

The sample gives $n = 50$, $\bar{x} = 0.577$ so the value of the test statistic is

$$z = \frac{0.577 - 0.580}{\frac{0.015}{\sqrt{50}}} = -1.414\ldots$$

This is *not* in the critical region so you accept H_0 and conclude that there is no significant evidence that the mean diameter has changed.

You could calculate the probability associated with this test and compare it with the significance level of 1%. In this example it would require

$$P(\bar{X} \leqslant 0.577) + P(\bar{X} \geqslant 0.583)$$

since a deviation of more than 0.003 from the value given in H_0 would constitute 'worse' evidence against H_0.

This equals to:
λ

$$\begin{aligned} & 2 \times P(\bar{X} \leqslant 0.577) \\ &= 2 \times P(Z \leqslant -1.41) \\ &= 2 \times (1 - 0.9207) \\ &= 0.1586 \end{aligned}$$

This is not a small probability, so you do not reject H_0. You can conclude that there is insufficient evidence of a change in the mean.

The following four steps might be helpful in answering questions about hypothesis tests for the mean μ.

1. Identify the sample mean $\bar{x}$ and a value for the population mean μ given by the null hypothesis.
2. Write down the null (H_0) and alternative (H_1) hypotheses. The alternative hypothesis will determine whether you want a one-tailed or a two-tailed test.
3. Calculate the value of the test statistic

$$z = \frac{\bar{x} - \mu}{\frac{\sigma}{\sqrt{n}}}$$

4. Either using the critical region for Z or by calculating a probability, complete the test and state your conclusions. The following points should be addressed:

(a) is the result significant or not?
(b) what are the implications in terms of the *context of the original problem?*

Exercise 2E

In each of questions 1–5 a sample of size n is taken from a population having a normal distribution with mean μ and variance σ^2. Test the hypotheses at the stated levels.

1 H_0: $\mu = 21$, H_1: $\mu \neq 21$, $n = 20$, $\bar{x} = 21.2$, $\sigma = 1.5$, at the 5% level

2 H_0: $\mu = 100$, H_1: $\mu < 100$, $n = 36$, $\bar{x} = 98.5$, $\sigma = 5.0$, at the 5% level

3 H_0: $\mu = 5$, H_1: $\mu \neq 5$, $n = 25$, $\bar{x} = 6.1$, $\sigma = 3.0$, at the 5% level

4 H_0: $\mu = 15$, H_1: $\mu > 15$, $n = 40$, $\bar{x} = 16.5$, $\sigma = 3.5$, at the 1% level

5 H_0: $\mu = 50$, H_1: $\mu \neq 50$, $n = 60$, $\bar{x} = 48.9$, $\sigma = 4.0$, at the 1% level

In each of questions 6–10 a sample of size n is taken from a population having a $N(\mu, \sigma^2)$ distribution. Find the critical regions for the test statistic $\bar{X}$ in the following tests.

6 H_0: $\mu = 120$, H_1: $\mu < 120$, $n = 30$, $\sigma = 2.0$, at the 5% level

7 H_0: $\mu = 12.5$, H_1: $\mu > 12.5$, $n = 25$, $\sigma = 1.5$, at the 1% level

8 H_0: $\mu = 85$, H_1: $\mu < 85$, $n = 50$, $\sigma = 4.0$, at the 10% level

9 H_0: $\mu = 0$, H_1: $\mu \neq 0$, $n = 45$, $\sigma = 3.0$, at the 5% level

10 H_0: $\mu = -8$, H_1: $\mu \neq -8$, $n = 20$, $\sigma = 1.2$, at the 1% level

11 The times taken for a capful of stain remover to remove a standard chocolate stain from a baby's bib are normally distributed with a mean of 185 s and a standard deviation of 15 s. The manufacturers of the stain remover claim to have developed a new formula which will shorten the time taken for a stain to be removed. A random sample of 25 capfuls of the new formula are tested and the mean time for the sample is 179 s. Test at the 5% level whether or not there is evidence that the new formula is an improvement.

12 The IQ scores of a population are normally distributed with a mean of 100 and standard deviation of 15. A psychologist wishes to test the theory that eating chocolate before sitting an IQ test improves your score. A random sample of 100 people are selected and they are each given a 100 g bar of chocolate to eat before taking a standard IQ test. Their mean score on the test was 102.5. Test the psychologist's theory at the 5% level.

13 The diameters of circular cardboard drinks mats produced by a certain machine are normally distributed with a mean of 9 cm and a standard deviation of 0.15 cm. After the machine is serviced a random sample of 30 mats is selected and their diameters are measured to see if the mean diameter has altered. The mean of the sample was 8.95 cm. Test, at the 5% level, whether there is significant evidence of a change in the mean diameter of mats produced by the machine.

14 Research workers measured the body lengths, in mm, of 10 specimens of fish spawn of a certain species off the coast of eastern Scotland and found these lengths to be

12.5 10.2 11.1 9.6 12.1 9.3 10.7 11.4 14.7 10.4

Obtain unbiased estimates for the mean and variance of the lengths of all such fish spawn off eastern Scotland.
Research shows that, for a very large number of specimens of spawn of this species off the coast of Wales, the mean body length is 10.2 mm. Assuming that the variance of the lengths of spawn off eastern Scotland is 2.56, perform a significance test at the 5% level to decide whether the mean body length of fish spawn off the coast of eastern Scotland is larger than that of fish spawn off the coast of Wales. [L]

15 Explain what you understand by the Central Limit Theorem.
An electrical firm claims that the average lifetime of the bulbs it produces is 800 hours with a standard deviation of 42 hours. To test this claim a random sample of 120 bulbs was taken and these bulbs were found to have an average lifetime of 789 hours. Stating clearly your hypotheses and using a 5% level of significance test the claim made by the electrical firm. [L]

2.7 Testing for a difference between two normal distributions

In chapter 8 of Book T1 you saw that if X_1 and X_2 are two independent normal distributions with means of μ_1 and μ_2 and standard deviations σ_1 and σ_2 respectively then

$$X_1 - X_2 \sim \mathrm{N}(\mu_1 - \mu_2, \sigma_1^2 + \sigma_2^2)$$

Now if $\bar{X}_1$ and $\bar{X}_2$ are sample means based on samples of size n_1 and n_2 respectively from the above two normal populations then:

$$\bar{X}_1 - \bar{X}_2 \sim \mathrm{N}\left(\mu_1 - \mu_2, \frac{\sigma_1^2}{n_1} + \frac{\sigma_2^2}{n_2}\right)$$

and the statistic $\bar{X}_1 - \bar{X}_2$ can be used to test hypotheses about the values of μ_1 and μ_2.

The central limit theorem tells you that, provided the sample sizes n_1 and n_2 are large, then $\bar{X}_1 - \bar{X}_2$ will have a normal distribution whatever the distributions of X_1 and X_2. You can therefore use this to test if there is a significant difference between the means of any two populations. The usual null hypothesis is that the values of μ_1 and μ_2 are equal, but other situations are possible provided that the null hypothesis gives you a value for $\mu_1 - \mu_2$, although such situations will not be studied in this book.

Example 10

The weights of boys and girls in a certain school are known to be normally distributed with standard deviations of 5 kg and 8 kg respectively. A random sample of 25 boys had a mean weight of 48 kg and a random sample of 30 girls had a mean weight of 45 kg. Is there any evidence that the mean weight of boys in the school is greater than the mean weight of the girls?

The question you are asked is whether $\mu_{\text{boy}} > \mu_{\text{girl}}$. This will not yield a value for '$\mu_1 - \mu_2$', so choose as your null hypothesis $\mu_{\text{boy}} = \mu_{\text{girl}}$ (in other words, if the mean weights are the *same* does the sample provide evidence to contradict this assumption?) and proceed as follows:

$$\mathrm{H}_0 : \mu_{\text{boy}} = \mu_{\text{girl}} \qquad \mathrm{H}_1 : \mu_{\text{boy}} > \mu_{\text{girl}}$$

Given the null hypothesis and $\sigma_1 = 5$, $n_1 = 25$, $\sigma_2 = 8$ and $n_2 = 30$:

$$\bar{X}_1 - \bar{X}_2 \sim \mathrm{N}\left(0, \frac{25}{25} + \frac{64}{30}\right)$$

The test statistic is:

$$z = \frac{\bar{x}_1 - \bar{x}_2}{\sqrt{\left(\frac{\sigma_1^2}{n_1} + \frac{\sigma_2^2}{n_2}\right)}}$$

$$= \frac{48 - 45}{\sqrt{\left(\frac{25}{25} + \frac{64}{30}\right)}}$$

$$= \frac{3}{\sqrt{3.1333\ldots}}$$

$$= 1.6947\ldots$$

The 5% (one-tailed) critical value for Z is $z = 1.6449$ (Table 4) so this value *is* significant and you can reject H_0 and conclude that there is evidence that the mean weight of boys is greater than the mean weight of the girls.

Example 11

A manufacturer of personal stereos could use batteries made by two different manufacturers. The standard deviation of lifetimes for '*Never Die*' batteries is 3.1 hours and for '*Everlasting*' batteries it is 2.9 hours. A random sample of 80 *Never Die* batteries and a random sample of 90 *Everlasting* batteries were tested and their mean lifetimes were 7.9 hours and 8.2 hours respectively. Test at the 5% level whether there is any evidence of a difference between the mean lifetimes of the two makes of batteries.

Let μ_1 be the mean lifetime of *Never Die* batteries and let μ_2 be the mean lifetime of *Everlasting* batteries.

Notice that you are looking for a *difference*, so a two-tailed test is appropriate.

$$H_0 : \mu_1 = \mu_2 \qquad H_1 : \mu_1 \neq \mu_2$$

$$\sigma_1 = 3.1,\ n_1 = 80,\ \sigma_2 = 2.9 \text{ and } n_2 = 90$$

$$\bar{x}_1 - \bar{x}_2 = 7.9 - 8.2 = -0.3$$

You are not told that the distributions of lifetimes of batteries are normally distributed but the sample sizes are both quite large and so by the central limit theorem you can proceed with $\bar{X}_1 - \bar{X}_2$ approximately normally distributed.

So:

$$z = \frac{\bar{x}_1 - \bar{x}_2}{\sqrt{\left(\frac{\sigma_1^2}{n_1} + \frac{\sigma_2^2}{n_2}\right)}}$$

$$= \frac{-0.3}{\sqrt{\left(\frac{(3.1)^2}{80} + \frac{(2.9)^2}{90}\right)}}$$

$$= -0.649\ldots$$

The 5% (two-tailed) critical values for Z are $z = \pm 1.9600$.

So this value is not significant and you do not reject H_0. You can conclude that there is no significant evidence of a difference in the mean lifetimes of the two makes of battery.

■ **Test for difference between two means**

If $X_1 \sim N(\mu_1, \sigma_1^2)$ and the independent random variable $X_2 \sim N(\mu_2, \sigma_2^2)$ then a test of the null hypothesis $H_0: \mu_1 = \mu_2$ can be carried out using the test statistic

$$\frac{\bar{X}_1 - \bar{X}_2}{\sqrt{\left(\frac{\sigma_1^2}{n_1} + \frac{\sigma_2^2}{n_2}\right)}} \sim N(0, 1^2)$$

If the sample sizes n_1 and n_2 are large then the result can be extended, by the central limit theorem, to include cases where the distributions of X_1 and X_2 are not normal.

One of the practical difficulties that you will encounter with these tests, and also in finding confidence intervals, is the need to know the value of the standard deviation. In practice, if you do not know μ it is unlikely that you will know σ. Sometimes it is reasonable to assume that a manufacturing process will have the same standard deviation but perhaps just have an altered mean. Occasionally you can look at historical data and see that over a period of time the standard deviation has been constant, and it may be reasonable to assume that it remains so in the present case, but often it may be impossible to say what σ is.

You saw earlier in this chapter (page 20) how to find an unbiased estimate for σ^2, namely s^2, and if you do not know σ then estimating it by s would seem a sensible idea. Your test statistic for a *single* sample would then be

$$\frac{\bar{X} - \mu}{\frac{s}{\sqrt{n}}}$$

Unfortunately, this statistic does not have a normal distribution. However, in situations where the distribution of the parent population is normal the distribution of this statistic is known and it is called Student's t distribution. It was discovered by the British statistician W. S. Gossett who worked for Guinness and published his work under the pseudonym of 'the Student'. But a knowledge of this distribution is outside the scope of this course. If the distribution of the parent population is *not* known, alternative *non-parametric* tests have to be used but these are again outside the scope of this course. However, there is a way out of this dead-end if the samples are large. If the population is normal or approximately normal then it can be shown that the statistic

$$\frac{\bar{X} - \mu}{\frac{s}{\sqrt{n}}}$$

is approximately distributed $N(0, 1^2)$, though you do not need to know how to prove this.

If the sample size is very large the estimate s that you are using for σ might reasonably be expected to be very close to σ and, given that a more precise test would almost certainly involve a level of knowledge beyond your present grasp, for very large samples the above statistic is usually *assumed* to have an approximate $N(0, 1^2)$ distribution. You must remember that such a test is an approximation and you should be wary of drawing strong conclusions from values of z close to the critical values. Often in these large-sample cases, although you may not know the population distribution it may be reasonable to assume that it is normal, or nearly so, in which case the result mentioned above can be invoked to add credibility to your test.

There is no simple answer to the question how large a sample must be, other than 'the larger the better'.

- **If the population is normal, or can be assumed to be so, then for large samples the statistic $\frac{\bar{X} - \mu}{\frac{s}{\sqrt{n}}}$ has an approximate $N(0, 1^2)$ distribution.**
- **If the population is not normal, by assuming that s is a close approximation to σ then $\frac{\bar{X} - \mu}{\frac{s}{\sqrt{n}}}$ can be treated as having an approximate $N(0, 1^2)$ distribution.**

These results can be used for hypothesis tests and confidence intervals.

Example 12

An experiment was conducted to compare the drying properties of two paints, Quickdry and Speedicover. In the experiment, 200 similar pieces of metal were painted, 100 randomly allocated to Quickdry and the rest to Speedicover.

The table below summarises the times, in minutes, taken for these pieces of metal to become touch-dry.

	Quickdry	*Speedicover*
Mean	28.7	30.6
Standard deviation	7.32	3.51

It is believed that the time taken for paint to become touch-dry is normally distributed.

The manufacturer of Quickdry claims that on average this paint takes 25 minutes to become touch-dry.

(a) Stating clearly your hypotheses and using a 5% significance level, test whether or not these data are consistent with the claim of the manufacturer.

(b) Using a 5% significance level, test whether or not the mean time for Quickdry to become touch-dry is less than that for Speedicover. State your hypotheses clearly.

(c) Suggest two reasons why the time for each paint to become touch-dry is not constant. [L]

As the samples are large and the populations are believed to be normally distributed, you can use the sample standard deviations instead of σ_1 and σ_2 and the test statistic will still have an approximately $\mathrm{N}(0, 1^2)$ distribution.

(a) $\mathrm{H}_0 : \mu_Q = 25 \qquad \mathrm{H}_1 : \mu_Q \neq 25$

$$n_Q = 100 \text{ and } s_Q = 7.32$$

The value of the test statistic is $z = \dfrac{28.7 - 25}{\frac{7.32}{\sqrt{100}}} = 5.05$

The 5% critical regions for Z are $Z \leqslant -1.96$ or $Z \geqslant 1.96$. This value of z is in the critical region so you reject H_0 and say that the data are not consistent with the manufacturer's claim.

It is worth pointing out that a one-tailed test could also be used in this part and the result would, of course, still be significant.

(b) $\mathrm{H}_0 : \mu_Q = \mu_S \qquad \mathrm{H}_1 : \mu_Q < \mu_S$ (one-tailed test)

$$n_Q = 100,\ s_Q = 7.32,\ n_S = 100 \text{ and } s_S = 3.51$$

The value of the test statistic is:

$$\begin{aligned} z &= \frac{\bar{x}_Q - \bar{x}_S}{\sqrt{\left(\frac{s_Q^2}{100} + \frac{s_S^2}{100}\right)}} \\ &= \frac{28.7 - 30.6}{\sqrt{\left(\frac{7.32^2}{100} + \frac{3.51^2}{100}\right)}} \\ &= -2.341 \end{aligned}$$

The 5% critical region for Z is $Z \leqslant -1.6449$ and -2.341 is in this critical region. So the result *is* significant and you can reject H_0 and conclude that there is evidence that the mean time for Quickdry to become touch-dry is less than the mean time for Speedicover.

(c) The drying conditions; for example, room temperature and wind flow would affect the drying time, as would the thickness of the paint.

2.8 Interpreting a hypothesis test

Throughout this part of the chapter we have been careful to avoid saying that you accept the null hypothesis but rather that you *reject* it or *do not reject* it. If a test gives a significant result then the conclusion is clear: you reject the null hypothesis and *accept* the alternative hypothesis. But what if the value of the test statistic is not significant? This means that the evidence of the sample *in this case* was not sufficient to cause you to reject H_0. It does *not* mean that H_0 is true but simply that it remains as a hypothesis (i.e. a proposed but unproven value of μ). Some textbooks talk about 'accepting' the null hypothesis when a test gives a non-significant result. It is important to remember that this does not mean that the null hypothesis is *proven* but simply that it can be 'accepted' as a working hypothesis *at the moment*. The null hypothesis has survived this time, but a later sample may cause you to reject it. This is how mathematical modelling progresses: a model is proposed and used until it is found wanting, and then the model is refined and used, tested and perhaps refined further.

In the case of example 8 (p. 42) a sample mean $\bar{x}$ of 71.2 would not give a significant result. You cannot say that $\mu = 70$ but if further information about the value of μ is required then you could use the sample to obtain a 95% confidence interval for μ. This would give

$$71.2 \pm 1.96 \times \frac{7.5}{\sqrt{90}}$$

$$= (69.7, 72.7)$$

In practice, if more information is required about the value of μ then a further sample could be taken.

Exercise 2F

In questions 1–3 carry out a test on the given hypotheses. The populations from which the samples are drawn are normally distributed.

1 H_0: $\mu_1 = \mu_2$; H_1: $\mu_1 > \mu_2$; $n_1 = 15$, $\sigma_1 = 5.0$, $n_2 = 20$, $\sigma_2 = 4.8$, $\bar{x}_1 = 23.8$ and $\bar{x}_2 = 21.5$ using a 5% level

2 H_0: $\mu_1 = \mu_2$; H_1: $\mu_1 \neq \mu_2$; $n_1 = 30$, $\sigma_1 = 4.2$, $n_2 = 25$, $\sigma_2 = 3.6$, $\bar{x}_1 = 49.6$ and $\bar{x}_2 = 51.7$ using a 5% level

3 H_0: $\mu_1 = \mu_2$; H_1: $\mu_1 < \mu_2$; $n_1 = 25$, $\sigma_1 = 0.81$, $n_2 = 36$, $\sigma_2 = 0.75$, $\bar{x}_1 = 3.62$ and $\bar{x}_2 = 4.11$ using a 1% level

In questions 4–6 carry out a test on the given hypotheses. What is the significance of the central limit theorem in these three questions?

4 H_0: $\mu_1 = \mu_2$; H_1: $\mu_1 \neq \mu_2$; $n_1 = 85$, $\sigma_1 = 8.2$, $n_2 = 100$, $\sigma_2 = 11.3$, $\bar{x}_1 = 112.0$ and $\bar{x}_2 = 108.1$ using a 1% level

5 H_0: $\mu_1 = \mu_2$; H_1: $\mu_1 > \mu_2$; $n_1 = 100$, $\sigma_1 = 18.3$, $n_2 = 150$, $\sigma_2 = 15.4$, $\bar{x}_1 = 72.6$ and $\bar{x}_2 = 69.5$ using a 5% level

6 H_0: $\mu_1 = \mu_2$; H_1: $\mu_1 < \mu_2$; $n_1 = 120$, $\sigma_1 = 0.013$, $n_2 = 90$, $\sigma_2 = 0.015$, $\bar{x}_1 = 0.863$ and $\bar{x}_2 = 0.868$ using a 1% level

7 A certain factory has two machines designed to cut piping. The first machine works to a standard deviation of 0.011 cm and the second machine has a standard deviation of 0.015 cm. A random sample of 10 pieces of piping from the first machine has a mean length of 6.531 cm and a random sample of 15 pieces from the second machine has a length of 6.524 cm. Assuming that the lengths of piping follow a normal distribution, test, at the 5% level, whether or not the machines are producing piping of the same mean length.

8 A certain health authority set up an investigation to examine the ages of mothers when they give birth to their first children. A random sample of 250 first-time mothers from a certain year had a mean age of 22.45 years with a standard deviation of 2.9 years. A further random sample of 280 first-time mothers taken 10 years later had a mean age of 22.96 years with a standard deviation of 2.8 years.

(a) Test whether or not these figures suggest that there is a difference in the mean age of first-time mothers between these two dates.

(b) State any assumptions you have made about the distribution of ages of first-time mothers.

9 It is claimed that the masses of components produced in a small factory have a mean mass of 10 g. A random sample of 250 of these components are tested and the sample mean, $\bar{x}$, is 9.88 g and the standard deviation is 1.12 g.

(a) Test, at the 5% level, whether or not there has been a change in the mean mass of a component.

(b) State any assumptions you would make to carry out this test.

10 The breaking stresses of rubber bands are normally distributed. A company uses bands with a mean breaking stress of 46.50N. A new supplier claims that they can supply bands that are stronger and provides a sample of 100 bands for the company to test. The company checked the breaking stress x for each of these 100 bands and the results are summarised as follows:

$$n = 100 \qquad \Sigma x = 4715 \qquad \Sigma x^2 = 222\,910$$

(a) Test, at the 5% level, whether or not there is evidence that the new bands are better.

(b) Find an approximate 95% confidence interval for the mean breaking stress of these new rubber bands.

11 A shopkeeper complains that the average weight of chocolate bars of a certain type that he is buying from a wholesaler is less than the stated value of 8.50 g. The shopkeeper weighed 100

bars from a large delivery and found that their weights had a mean of 8.36 g and a standard deviation of 0.72 g. Using a 5% significance level, determine whether or not the shopkeeper is justified in his complaint. State clearly the null and alternative hypotheses that you are using, and express your conclusion in words.
Obtain, to 2 decimal places, the limits of a 98% confidence interval for the mean weight of the chocolate bars in the shopkeeper's delivery. [L]

12 On each of 100 days a conservationist took a sample of 1 litre of water from a particular place along a river, and measured the amount, x mg, of chlorine in the sample. The results she obtained are shown in the table.

x	1	2	3	4	5	6	7	8	9
Number of days	4	8	20	22	16	13	10	6	1

Calculate the mean amount of chlorine present per litre of water, and estimate, to 3 decimal places, the standard error of this mean.
Obtain approximate 98% confidence limits for the mean amount of chlorine present per litre of water.
Given that measurements at the same point under the same conditions are taken for a further 100 days, estimate, to 3 decimal places, the probability that the mean of these measurements will be greater than 4.6 mg per litre of water. [L]

13 The amount, to the nearest mg, of a certain chemical in particles in the atmosphere at a meteorological station was measured each day for 300 days. The results are shown in the table.

Amount of chemical in the atmosphere

Amount of chemical (mg)	12	13	14	15	16
Number of days	5	42	210	31	12

Find the mean daily amount of chemical over the 300 days and estimate, to 2 decimal places, its standard error.

Obtain, to 2 decimal places, approximate 98% confidence limits for the mean daily amount of chemical in the atmosphere.
If daily measurements are taken for a further 300 days, estimate, to 2 decimal places, the probability that the mean of these daily measurements will be less than 14. [L]

2.9 Type I and type II errors

Occasionally miscarriages of justice take place and these are often widely publicised in the news. Ideally, we should like to avoid making any such errors, but because the system that we are using involves probability 'beyond reasonable doubt' then there is some chance of an error creeping in and the best that we can do is to try and keep the probability of these errors small. These miscarriages of justice fall into two categories.

The most commonly publicised miscarriage of justice is when a defendant is convicted but is, in fact, innocent. In terms of our hypothesis tests this is to

'reject H_0 when H_0 is true'

and we call this a **type I error**.

On page 42 in example 8 we considered the weights of students when they joined a college and were interested in whether or not the mean weight of the new entry was higher than the usual mean weight. The null and alternative hypotheses were

$$H_0 : \mu = 70 \quad \text{and} \quad H_1 : \mu > 70$$

and the significance level was 5%. We found the critical region for $\bar{X}$ to be $\bar{X} \geqslant 71.30$. In this case a type I error is when you reject H_0 but in fact H_0 is true; you accept H_1 and conclude that the mean weight of the new entry is more than 70 kg when in fact it *is* 70 kg. In other words,

$$\text{P(type I error)} = \text{P}(\bar{X} \geqslant 71.30 | \mu = 70)$$

But this is simply 0.05 or the significance level of the test, since the critical region $\bar{X} \geqslant 71.30$ was found from the calculation

$$\text{P}(Z \geqslant 1.6449) = 0.05$$

So: $$\frac{\bar{X}-\mu}{\frac{\sigma}{\sqrt{n}}} \geqslant 1.6449$$

that is: $$\bar{X} \geqslant 1.6449 \times \frac{7.5}{\sqrt{90}} + 70$$

or $$\bar{X} \geqslant 71.300\ldots.$$

The significance level, you will recall, is the 'threshold' probability for rejection of H_0; assuming that H_0 is true, if the probability of evidence 'as bad or worse' is as small or smaller than this probability then H_0 is rejected. In the case of a test using a continuous distribution such as the normal distribution, the significance level and the probability of a type I error are both the same and give you the probability of obtaining a wrongful conviction.

The '|' notation was used in Book T1, chapter 5, to describe conditional probabilities and here the statement $P(\bar{X} \geqslant 71.30 | \mu = 70)$ means the probability that $\bar{X} \geqslant 71.30$ *given that* the true value of the mean μ is 70.

- **A type I error occurs when H_0 is rejected when it is in fact true. The probability of a type I error is the probability of obtaining a value of the test statistic that lies in the critical region assuming that H_0 is true. When the distribution of the test statistic is continuous then this probability will equal the significance level of the test.**

The other sort of mistake that can be made under such a judicial system is when the defendant is *not* convicted even though he or she is guilty: the case where the murderer gets let off. In terms of a hypothesis test this is the situation where you

'do not reject H_0 when H_1 is true'

and this called a **type II error**.

To calculate the probability of a type II error you would need to know the true value of μ, because the alternative hypothesis H_1 gives a *range* of values for μ (e.g. $\mu > 70$). Without a specific value of μ you cannot calculate the probability of not rejecting H_0. In the above situation you would require $P(\bar{X} < 71.30)$ since H_0 is rejected for $\bar{X} \geqslant 71.30$. Suppose in the above example the true value of μ is in fact 71; in other words, the mean weight of the new entry is in fact higher, at 71 kg. In order to make a type II error you would have to not reject the hypothesis that $\mu = 70$ when in fact it is 71. In terms of the test, you would have

$$\begin{aligned}
\text{P(type II error)} &= \text{P}(\bar{X} < 71.30 | \mu = 71) \\
&= \text{P}\left(Z < \frac{71.30 - 71}{\frac{7.5}{\sqrt{90}}}\right) \\
&= \text{P}(Z < 0.379\ldots) \\
&= 0.65 \text{ (2 d.p.)}
\end{aligned}$$

Of course, if you *did* know the true value of μ then there would be no need to carry out a test anyway. Statisticians sometimes plot the type II error against various values of μ to examine the nature of a particular test. The study of these curves, sometimes called operating characteristic curves, is beyond the scope of this course. All that is required here is the ability to calculate type I and type II errors as illustrated in the example below.

Example 13

The weight of jam in a jar, measured in grams, is distributed normally with a mean of 150 and a standard deviation of 5. The production process occasionally leads to a change in the mean weight of jam per jar but the standard deviation remains unaltered. The manager monitors the production process and for every new batch takes a random sample of 25 jars and weighs their contents to see if there has been any reduction in the mean weight of jam per jar. Find the critical values for the test statistic $\bar{X}$, the mean weight of jam in a sample of 25 jars, using
(a) a 5% level of significance
(b) a 1% level of significance.

Given that the true value of μ for the new batch is in fact 147,
(c) find the probability of a type II error for each of the above critical regions.

$H_0 : \mu = 150$ $\quad$ $H_1 : \mu < 150$ $\quad$ (i.e. a one-tailed test)

$$n = 25 \text{ and } \sigma = 5$$

(a) The 5% critical region for Z is $Z \leqslant -1.6449$ so

reject H_0 if $$\frac{\bar{X} - 150}{\frac{5}{\sqrt{25}}} \leqslant -1.6449$$

That is, the critical region for $\bar{X}$ is

$$\bar{X} \leqslant \frac{5}{\sqrt{25}} \times (-1.6449) + 150$$

so $$\bar{X} \leqslant 148.3551$$

(b) The 1% critical region for Z is $Z \leqslant -2.3263$ so

reject H_0 if $$\frac{\bar{X} - 150}{\frac{5}{\sqrt{25}}} \leqslant -2.3263$$

That is, the critical region for $\bar{X}$ is

$$\bar{X} \leqslant \frac{5}{\sqrt{25}} \times (-2.3263) + 150$$

so $$\bar{X} \leqslant 147.6737$$

(c) 5% test

$$\begin{aligned}
\text{P(type II error)} &= \text{P}(\bar{X} > 148.3551 | \mu = 147) \\
&= \text{P}\left(Z > \frac{148.3551 - 147}{\frac{5}{\sqrt{25}}}\right) \\
&= \text{P}(Z > 1.3551) \quad \text{[use 1.36]} \\
&= 1 - 0.9131 \\
&= 0.087 \text{ (3 d.p.)}
\end{aligned}$$

1% test

$$\begin{aligned}
\text{P(type II error)} &= \text{P}(\bar{X} > 147.6737 | \mu = 147) \\
&= \text{P}\left(Z > \frac{147.6737 - 147}{\frac{5}{\sqrt{25}}}\right) \\
&= \text{P}(Z > 0.6737) \quad \text{[use 0.67]} \\
&= 1 - 0.7486 \\
&= 0.251 \text{ (3 d.p.)}
\end{aligned}$$

Notice how in this example if we try to *reduce* P(type I error) then P(type II error) *increases*. A more detailed study of the interplay between these two probabilities is beyond the scope of this course. But you should be aware of this phenomenon and therefore able to appreciate one of the reasons why we do not always use a significance level that is very small. The value of 5% has already been mentioned as a commonly used level and in a situation where a particular significance level is not prescribed then this value is recommended.

Exercise 2G

1 Carry out the following hypothesis tests assuming a normal distribution.

(a) H_0: $\mu = 50$; H_1: $\mu > 50$; $\sigma = 3$, $\bar{x} = 52$, $n = 20$, and use a 1% significance level
If in fact $\mu = 53$, find the probability of a type II error.

(b) H_0: $\mu = 45$; H_1: $\mu < 45$; $\sigma = 5$, $\bar{x} = 44$, $n = 30$, and use a 10% significance level
If in fact $\mu = 46$, find the probability of a type II error.

(c) H_0: $\mu = 20.5$; H_1: $\mu \neq 20.5$; $\sigma = 0.5$, $\bar{x} = 20.75$, $n = 36$, and use a 5% significance level

If in fact $\mu = 20.6$, find the probability of a type II error.

(d) H_0: $\mu = 30$; H_1: $\mu \neq 30$; $\sigma = 2$, $\bar{x} = 31$, $n = 20$, and use a 1% significance level

If in fact $\mu = 32$, find the probability of a type II error.

2 (a) Carry out the following hypothesis test, assuming a normal distribution.

H_0: $\mu = 40$; H_1: $\mu < 40$; $\sigma = 4$, $\bar{x} = 38$, $n = 16$, and use a 5% significance level

(b) Find the probability of making a type II error in the cases where μ is (i) 30 (ii) 35 (iii) 40 (iv) 45.

Plot these points on a rough graph of probability of type II error against μ.

(c) Repeat parts (a) and (b) using a 1% significance level.

3 A manufacturer claims that the average length of tubes produced by his factory is 20 cm. The length of a tube has a normal distribution with standard deviation 2 cm. A sample of 36 tubes has a mean length of 19.5 cm.

(a) Test, at the 5% level, whether there is significant evidence of a change in average length.

(b) The manufacturer decides to take a sample of 25 tubes from each batch produced in order to monitor the process. Using a 5% level find the critical values of $\bar{x}$ that would determine whether he rejects the batch. (Assume a two-tailed test.)

(c) Suppose the average length of a tube has increased to 21 cm. What is the probability that the manufacturer would *accept* the batch believing the mean to be 20 cm?

4 The number of words that a secretary can type in one minute follows a normal distribution with mean 60 and standard deviation 15. An office furniture manufacturer claims that their new typist's chair will improve a typist's speed.

(a) A random sample of 30 secretaries try these new chairs and the average number of words they type per minute, $\bar{x}$, is found. Using a 5% test find the critical value of $\bar{x}$.

(b) A consumer organisation tests these chairs on 30 secretaries and finds their sample mean (number of words per minute) is 67 words. What should the organisation recommend?

(c) If the mean number of words per minute after using this new chair is in fact 65, find the probability of making a type II error in using this test.

(d) The manufacturer wishes to change the probability of a type II error. Explain whether he would wish to increase or decrease this probability and why.

(e) Give an example, using the 5% level, of a different testing procedure which is likely to satisfy the manufacturer's aims. (Assume μ for the new chair is in fact 65.)

2.10 Hypothesis test for the proportion *p* of a binomial distribution

The standard treatment for a particular disease has a probability $\frac{2}{5}$ of success. A certain doctor has undertaken research in this area and has produced a new drug which has been successful in 11 out of 20 patients upon whom he has tested it. The doctor claims that the new drug represents an improvement on the standard treatment and is trying to sell his formula to a large drug company.

Is the doctor's claim justified? To answer this question you can set the problem up as a hypothesis test about the proportion p of the population of people with this disease for whom the drug is successful. The null hypothesis will be that $p = \frac{2}{5}$, that is, that there is no change, and the doctor's claim is that $p > \frac{2}{5}$. So you have:

$$\mathrm{H}_0 : p = \tfrac{2}{5} \qquad \mathrm{H}_1 : p > \tfrac{2}{5}$$

If the null hypothesis is true then the random variable X representing the number of patients for whom the new drug was successful has a $\mathrm{B}(20, 0.4)$ distribution.

The value of X observed is $x = 11$ and values of X 'as bad or worse' would be $X \geqslant 11$ so the probability you need to calculate is

$$\begin{aligned} \mathrm{P}(X \geqslant 11) &= 1 - \mathrm{P}(X \leqslant 10) \\ &= 1 - 0.8725 \text{ (from Table 1)} \\ &= 0.1275 \end{aligned}$$

This probability is quite large (it is greater than 5%) and so you do not reject H_0.

The doctor might ask how many successful cases would be needed to obtain a significant result at the 5% level. To answer this question you need to find the critical values for the statistic X. Now you have

$$H_0 : p = \tfrac{2}{5} \qquad H_1 : p > \tfrac{2}{5}$$

so you want to find a value c so that

$$P(X \geqslant c) \leqslant 0.05$$

Table 1 at the back of this book gives values for $P(X \leqslant x)$, so you need to replace $P(X \geqslant c)$ by $1 - P(X \leqslant c - 1)$ to obtain

$$1 - P(X \leqslant c - 1) \leqslant 0.05$$

or $$0.95 \leqslant P(X \leqslant c - 1)$$

Now Table 1 (with $n = 20$ and $p = 0.4$) gives:

$$P(X \leqslant 11) = 0.9435$$
$$P(X \leqslant 12) = 0.9790$$

so in this case you have $\quad c - 1 = 12$

and therefore $\quad c = 13$

So the doctor would need at least 13 cases to obtain significant evidence against H_0.

It is also worth pointing out that in this case, since the binomial distribution is *discrete* and you have therefore had to round your critical value to the nearest appropriate integer, the P(type I error) will not equal the significance level of the test. A type I error, you will recall (see page 56), occurs when you reject H_0 when in fact H_0 is true. In this case if you assume $p = 0.4$ then you reject H_0 if $X \geqslant 13$ and

$$\begin{aligned} P(X \geqslant 13) &= 1 - P(X \leqslant 12) \\ &= 1 - 0.9790 \\ &= 0.021 \end{aligned}$$

Type II errors can also be calculated fairly easily. Suppose that you knew that the real success rate for the new drug was in fact 0.50. Then

$$\begin{aligned} \text{P(type II error)} &= P(X \leqslant 12 | p = 0.5) \\ &= 0.8684 \end{aligned}$$

Sometimes a two-tailed test may be required and the procedure is a simple extension of the one-tailed case.

Example 14

A psychologist is attempting to help a pupil improve his short-term memory. One of the tests the psychologist uses is to present the pupil with a tray of 10 objects and let him look at them for 1 minute before taking the tray away and asking the pupil to write down as many of the objects as he can. Over a period of several weeks the psychologist has ascertained that the proportion, p, of objects that the pupil remembers is 0.35. The pupil has just been on a long adventure holiday and the psychologist is interested to see if there has been any change in p. Find the critical values for a two-tailed test using a 5% significance level.

Let X represent the number of objects the pupil remembers.

$$H_0 : p = 0.35 \qquad H_1 : p \neq 0.35$$

Assuming H_0 is true then $X \sim B(10, 0.35)$.

For a two-tailed test at 5% level you require the values c_1 and c_2 so that

$$P(X \leqslant c_1) \leqslant 0.025 \quad \text{and} \quad P(X \geqslant c_2) \leqslant 0.025$$

From Table 1: $\quad P(X \leqslant 0) = 0.0135$

and $\quad P(X \leqslant 1) = 0.0860$

so the value of c_1 is 0.

Also: $\quad P(X \geqslant 7) = 1 - P(X \leqslant 6) = 1 - 0.9740 = 0.0260$

and $\quad P(X \geqslant 8) = 1 - P(X \leqslant 7) = 1 - 0.9952 = 0.0048$

so the value of c_2 is 8.

Thus the critical region for X is $X = 0$ or $X \geqslant 8$.

Because we are dealing with discrete distributions the values of X have to be taken to the nearest integer. This sometimes leads to awkward results, especially with two-tailed tests. If the value of p given by H_0 is not $\frac{1}{2}$ then the distribution of the test statistic X will not be symmetrical and the decision to choose the critical values to give a $2\frac{1}{2}$% rejection rate at each end can appear to be somewhat arbitrary. The final tests that result will usually not have a P(type I error) equal to the significance level and this can mean that the level at which the test is *actually* being carried out can be quite different from the intended one.

In example 14

$$\begin{aligned} \text{P(type I error)} &= P(X = 0 | p = 0.35) + P(X \geqslant 8 | p = 0.35) \\ &= 0.0135 + 0.0048 \\ &= 0.0183 \end{aligned}$$

and this is not very close to the 5% significance level required. You will notice that if you included 7 in your critical region and defined the critical region for the test as:

$$X = 0 \text{ or } X \geqslant 7$$

then:

$$\begin{aligned}\text{P(type I error)} &= \text{P}(X = 0 | p = 0.35) + \text{P}(X \geqslant 7 | p = 0.35) \\ &= 0.0135 + 0.0260 \\ &= 0.0395\end{aligned}$$

which is closer to the 5% significance level required.

It is usual practice, if a 5% two-tailed test is required, to use $2\frac{1}{2}\%$ at each end as given in example 14, but sometimes a slightly different critical region can be found if the test with P(type I error) as close as possible to 0.05 is required.

It is clear that these small-sample tests are somewhat crude and for ease of use they require tables of cumulative probabilities for the binomial distribution. If the number of trials is large, and the value of p is reasonably close to $\frac{1}{2}$, then the binomial distribution can be approximated by a normal distribution as was seen in Book T1, chapter 8. In this case the difficulty referred to in the previous paragraph will no longer apply.

The usual approach is to use the random variable $R = \dfrac{X}{n}$ as the proportion out of n trials that are successful.

If $X \sim \text{B}(n, p)$ then (see Book T1, chapter 7):

$$\text{E}(X) = np \quad \text{and} \quad \text{Var}(X) = np(1 - p)$$

So:

$$\text{E}(R) = \frac{np}{n} = p$$

and

$$\sigma^2 = \text{Var}(R) = \frac{np(1-p)}{n^2} = \frac{p(1-p)}{n}$$

Now if n is large you can approximate the distribution of R by a normal distribution and use

$$R \sim \text{N}(p, \sigma^2)$$

to carry out the test.

Example 15

A student is examining the probabilities associated with a traditional drawing pin. She has read in a book that the probability, p, that a drawing pin lands 'point up' when dropped onto a table is 0.35. She decides to test this theory and drops a drawing pin 400 times. The pin lands 'point up' on 153 occasions. Test, at the 5% level, whether or not there is evidence that p is greater than 0.35.

$$H_0 : p = 0.35 \qquad H_1 : p > 0.35$$

If R represents the proportion of times a drawing pin lands 'point up' then, assuming H_0 is true,

$$E(R) = p = 0.35$$

and $$\text{Var}(R) = \frac{p(1-p)}{n} = \frac{0.35 \times 0.65}{400} = 0.000\,568\,75$$

The observed value r of R is

$$r = \frac{153}{400} = 0.3825$$

Since the sample is quite large you can assume that R has a normal distribution, so the test statistic is

$$Z = \frac{R - p}{\sqrt{\left(\frac{p(1-p)}{n}\right)}}$$

i.e. $$z = \frac{0.3825 - 0.35}{\sqrt{0.000\,568\,75}} = 1.362\ldots$$

The one-tailed 5% critical value for Z is 1.6449 so this value is not significant and you do not reject the hypothesis that $p = 0.35$.

You can also tackle this example and these tests for the value of p by using the statistic X which represents the number of successes, or in this case the number of times the drawing pin lands 'point up'. You would have the same hypotheses and proceed as follows:

$$H_0 : p = 0.35 \qquad H_1 : p > 0.35$$

Assuming H_0 is true: $E(X) = np = 400 \times 0.35 = 140$

and $\text{Var}(X) = np(1-p) = 400 \times 0.35 \times 0.65 = 91$

The observed value of X is $x = 153$.

Now X will have a binomial distribution, but since n is large (and p is close to $\frac{1}{2}$) you can approximate the distribution of X by a normal distribution, and a continuity correction (see Book T1, chapter 8) should be applied.

Use the test statistic $$Z = \frac{X - p}{\sqrt{[np(1-p)]}}$$

As you have an upper one-tailed test, in other words the 'as bad or worse' cases for X are $X \geqslant 153$, the continuity correction gives $x = 152.5$ so the test statistic has the value

$$z = \frac{152.5 - 140}{\sqrt{91}}$$
$$= 1.310 \ldots$$

The critical region for Z is $Z \geqslant 1.6449$ so this value is not significant (it is not in the critical region) and once again you do not reject the null hypothesis.

Exercise 2H

Carry out the following tests using the binomial distribution where the random variable X represents the number of successes.

1. H_0: $p = 0.25$; H_1: $p > 0.25$; $n = 10$, $x = 5$ and using a 5% level of significance
2. H_0: $p = 0.40$; H_1: $p < 0.40$; $n = 10$, $x = 1$ and using a 5% level of significance
3. H_0: $p = 0.30$; H_1: $p > 0.30$; $n = 20$, $x = 10$ and using a 5% level of significance
4. H_0: $p = 0.45$; H_1: $p < 0.45$; $n = 20$, $x = 3$ and using a 1% level of significance
5. H_0: $p = 0.50$; H_1: $p \neq 0.50$; $n = 20$, $x = 7$ and using a 10% level of significance

Find the critical regions for the test statistic X representing the number of successes for the following tests. In each case calculate the probability of a type I error.

6. H_0: $p = 0.20$; H_1: $p > 0.20$; $n = 10$, using a 5% level of significance
7. H_0: $p = 0.15$; H_1: $p < 0.15$; $n = 20$, using a 5% level of significance
8. H_0: $p = 0.35$; H_1: $p > 0.35$; $n = 10$, using a 1% level of significance
9. H_0: $p = 0.40$; H_1: $p \neq 0.40$; $n = 20$, using a 5% level of significance
10. H_0: $p = 0.10$; H_1: $p > 0.10$; $n = 20$, using a 1% level of significance
11. For the test in question 6 calculate the probability of a type II error if $p = 0.30$.

12 For the test in question 7 calculate the probability of a type II error if $p = 0.10$.

13 For the test in question 8 calculate the probability of a type II error if $p = 0.45$.

14 For the test in question 9 calculate the probability of a type II error if $p = 0.35$.

15 For the test in question 10 calculate the probability of a type II error if $p = 0.15$.

16 The manufacturer of 'Supergold' margarine claims that people prefer this to butter. As part of an advertising campaign he asked five people to taste a sample of Supergold and a sample of butter and say which one they prefer. Four people chose Supergold. Assess the manufacturer's claim in the light of this evidence.

17 I tossed a coin 20 times and obtained a head on 6 occasions. Is there evidence that the coin is biased? Use a 5% two-tailed significance test.

18 A seed merchant usually keeps her stock in carefully monitored conditions. After the Christmas holidays one year she discovered that the monitoring system had broken down and there was a danger that the seed might have been damaged by frost. She decided to check a sample of 10 seeds to see if the proportion p that germinated had been reduced from the usual value of 0.85. Find the critical region for a one-tailed test using a 5% significance level.

19 A die used in playing a board game is supected of not giving the number 6 often enough. During a particular game it was rolled 12 times and only 1 six appeared. Does this represent significant evidence that the probability of a six on this die is less than $\frac{1}{6}$?

20 The 'Blue' party claim that they have 23% of the voters in a certain constituency supporting them. An opinion pollster asks a sample of 256 people whether or not they support the Blue party and finds 51 who say that they do. Test at the 5% significance level whether or not the Blue party are overstating their level of support.

21 A road safety investigation aims to test the hypothesis that 15% of cyclists on the road have brakes that are unsafe. The

investigating team believe that the proportion with unsafe brakes is in fact much higher. The plan is to stop a random sample of 800 cyclists and investigate their brakes. Using a 5% level, find the critical region for the test statistic X defined as the number of cyclists stopped with deficient brakes.

What would your conclusion be if 146 cyclists are found to have deficient brakes?

22 A recent survey claimed that 80% of households with children of school age owned a computer. The 230 students in a certain junior school were each asked if they had a computer at home and 167 said that they did. Test, at the 1% level, whether or not this sample is compatible with the survey.

What conclusion might you draw about this particular junior school?

23 A new drug to stop asthma attacks is considered to be effective if an attack is completely relieved within 5 minutes. It is claimed that the drug is effective in 1 out of 6 attacks. Given that 8 sufferers are given the drug during an attack, find, to 3 decimal places, the probability that, if the claim is true,

(a) at least two

(b) less than three

of the sufferers will find the drug effective.

In hospital trials on 120 sufferers, only 15 found the drug effective during an attack. Investigate, stating carefully your null hypothesis and your level of significance, whether this is sufficient evidence or not for rejecting the claim in favour of the alternative that the drug is effective in fewer than 1 in 6 attacks.

[L]

24 The success rate of the standard treatment for patients suffering from a particular skin disease is known to be 68%.

(a) In a sample of n patients, X is the number for which the treatment is successful. Write down a suitable distribution to model X. Give the reasons for your choice of distribution.

(b) A random sample of 10 patients receives the standard treatment. Find, to 3 decimal places, the probability that for exactly 6 patients the treatment will be successful.

(c) A new treatment is tried on a random sample of 100 patients with this disease. The treatment is successful for 75 of these patients. Perform a significance test at the 5% level to decide whether or not there is evidence that the success rate has increased. [L]

25 Over a long period of time it has been found that in Enrico's restaurant the ratio of non-vegetarian to vegetarian meals ordered is 3 to 1.

During one particular day at Enrico's restaurant, a random sample of 20 people contained 2 who ordered a vegetarian meal.

(a) Carry out a significance test to determine whether or not the proportion of vegetarian meals ordered that day is lower than is usual. State clearly your hypotheses and use a 10% significance level.

In Manuel's restaurant, of a random sample of 100 people ordering meals, 31 ordered vegetarian meals.

(b) Set up null and alternative hypotheses and, using a suitable approximation, test whether or not the proportion of people eating vegetarian meals at Manuel's is different from that at Enrico's restaurant. Use a 5% level of significance.

[L]

2.11 Hypothesis test for the mean of a Poisson distribution

You have seen how you can test the value of the mean from a normal population and how to apply the same principles to a discrete distribution, namely the binomial. It is a simple extension to test for the mean of a Poisson distribution.

Example 16

Accidents used to occur at a certain road junction at a rate of 6 per month. The residents had petitioned for traffic lights but the planners believed that the average number of accidents per month could be reduced simply by erecting a warning sign. In the month following the erection of the warning sign there were only 3 accidents. Does this give significant evidence that the planners were correct? Use a 5% level of significance.

If you let the random variable X represent the number of accidents in a month and λ represent the average number of accidents per month, then you have observed $x = 3$ and hypotheses can be formulated in terms of λ as follows:

$H_0 : \lambda = 6$ (i.e. no change) $H_1 : \lambda < 6$ (i.e. fewer accidents)

Assuming that H_0 is true you require $P(X \leqslant 3)$ since evidence 'as bad or worse' for the null hypothesis will mean 3 or fewer accidents in a month.

From Table 2 (remembering that the parameter λ for a Poisson distribution is equal to the mean μ):

$$P(X \leqslant 3 | \lambda = 6) = 0.1512$$

This is more than 5% so you do not reject H_0. The planners have not won their case and overturned the hypothesis that $\lambda = 6$.

In practice, of course, in a situation like this a much larger sample would probably be considered, say over a six-month period, and then the values of λ would be quite large and a normal approximation could be considered as in Book T1, chapter 8.

As in the case of the tests for the proportion using a binomial distribution, you can formulate tests in terms of the critical region for the random variable X and then find probabilities of type I and type II errors. In example 16 you can find the critical region for X as follows.

In order to reject H_0 the planners require a value c such that

$$P(X \leqslant c | \lambda = 6) \leqslant 0.05$$

From Table 2, with $\lambda = 6$:

$$P(X \leqslant 2) = 0.0620$$

and

$$P(X \leqslant 1) = 0.0174$$

So the critical value c is 1 and the critical region for this test is $X \leqslant 1$.

A type I error occurs when you reject H_0 and H_0 is true and the probability of this happening is simply 0.0174. This is much smaller than the 5% significance level that you were aiming for.

If in fact the true value of λ is 4.5, then you can find the probability of a type II error. We do not reject H_0 if $X \geqslant 2$ so

$$\begin{aligned} P(\text{type II error} | \lambda = 4.5) &= P(X \geqslant 2 | \lambda = 4.5) \\ &= 1 - P(X \leqslant 1 | \lambda = 4.5) \\ &= 1 - 0.0611 \\ &= 0.9389 \end{aligned}$$

which is very large but, as we noted earlier, if P(type I error) is very small then P(type II error) may well be large.

Exercise 2I

For each of questions 1–3 carry out the following tests. You may assume that the random variable X has a Po(λ) distribution.

1 H_0: $\lambda = 8$; H_1: $\lambda < 8$; $x = 3$, using a 5% level of significance

2 H_0: $\lambda = 6.5$; H_1: $\lambda < 6.5$; $x = 2$, using a 1% level of significance

3 H_0: $\lambda = 5.5$; H_1: $\lambda > 5.5$; $x = 8$, using a 5% level of significance

For each of questions 4–6 find the critical region for the test statistic X given that X has a Po(λ) distribution.

4 H_0: $\lambda = 4$; H_1: $\lambda > 4$; using a 5% level of significance

5 H_0: $\lambda = 9$; H_1: $\lambda < 9$; using a 1% level of significance

6 H_0: $\lambda = 3.5$; H_1: $\lambda < 3.5$; using a 5% level of significance

7 Find P(type I error) and, if $\lambda = 5.5$, P(type II error) for the test in question 4.

8 Find P(type I error) and, if $\lambda = 7.5$, P(type II error) for the test in question 5.

9 Find P(type I error) and, if $\lambda = 2.5$, P(type II error) for the test in question 6.

10 Every year a statistics teacher takes her class out to observe the traffic passing the school gates during a Tuesday lunch hour. Over the years she has established that the average number of lorries passing the gates in a lunch hour is 7.5. During the course of the last 12 months a new bypass has been built and the number of lorries passing the school gates in this year's experiment was 4. Test, at the 5% level, whether or not the mean number of lorries passing the gates on a Tuesday lunch hour has been reduced.

11 Over a long period, John has found that the bus taking him to school arrives late on average 9 times per month. In the month following the start of new summer schedules, John finds that his bus arrives late 13 times. Assuming that the number of times the bus is late has a Poisson distribution, test, at the 5% level of significance, whether the new schedules have in fact increased the number of times on which the bus is late. State clearly your null and alternative hypotheses. [L]

SUMMARY OF KEY POINTS

1 The standard error of the mean $\frac{\sigma}{\sqrt{n}}$ or $\frac{s}{\sqrt{n}}$ is the standard deviation (or estimate of it) of the mean $\bar{X}$.

2 The statistic T is an unbiased estimator of the population parameter θ if

$$E(T) = \theta$$

Unbiased estimate for μ is

$$\bar{x} = \frac{\Sigma x}{n}$$

Unbiased estimate for σ^2 is

$$s^2 = \frac{1}{n-1}\sum(x-\bar{x})^2 = \frac{n}{n-1}\left(\frac{\Sigma x^2}{n} - \bar{x}^2\right)$$

3 The central limit theorem states that, for large samples, $\bar{X}$ is approximately $\sim N\left(\mu, \frac{\sigma^2}{n}\right)$ where $\mu = E(X)$ and $\sigma^2 = \text{Var}(X)$ and n is the sample size.

4 The 95% confidence interval for the mean μ is

$$\bar{x} \pm 1.96 \times \frac{\sigma}{\sqrt{n}}$$

4 A hypothesis test is a mathematical procedure to examine a value of a population parameter proposed by the null hypothesis H_0 compared with an alternative range of values as given by the alternative hypothesis H_1.

5 The critical region is the range of values of a test statistic T that would lead you to reject H_0.

6 Single-sample problems: If a random sample $X_1, X_2, \ldots X_n$ is selected from $N(\mu, \sigma^2)$ then

$$\bar{X} \sim N\left(\mu, \frac{\sigma^2}{n}\right)$$

$$\frac{\bar{X}-\mu}{\frac{\sigma}{\sqrt{n}}} \sim N(0, 1^2)$$

For large n:

$$\frac{\bar{X} - \mu}{\frac{s}{\sqrt{n}}} \text{ is approximately} \sim \mathrm{N}(0, 1^2)$$

7 Two-sample problems: if random samples of n_1 X's and n_2 Y's are selected, then under suitable conditions

$$\frac{\bar{X} - \bar{Y}}{\sqrt{\left(\frac{\sigma_1^2}{n_1} + \frac{\sigma_2^2}{n_2}\right)}} \sim \mathrm{N}(0, 1^2)$$

8 A type I error occurs when H_0 is rejected when it is in fact true.

For a continuous distribution

P(type I error) = significance level of the test

9 A type II error occurs when H_0 is not rejected when it is in fact false.

Review exercise 1

1 (a) Give one advantage and one disadvantage of using
(i) a census (ii) a sample survey.
(b) It is decided to take a sample of 100 from a population consisting of 5000 elements. Explain how you would obtain a simple random sample without replacement from this population. [L]

2 Write brief notes on
(a) simple random sampling
(b) systematic sampling.
Your notes should include a description of each method and an advantage and a disadvantage associated with it.

3 Explain briefly what is meant when we say that a sample is chosen at random from a given population.
A research worker wishes to investigate the amount spent per week per head on a specific basic food in a particular district. He decides to take a sample of 200 shoppers chosen by one of the following methods:
(a) choosing every tenth person in a particular shopping street in that district between 9 a.m. and 11 a.m.
(b) obtaining the district electoral register and selecting 200 households using a table of random numbers.
State which of these methods you consider he should use to obtain the more reliable information about the population of interest, explaining as fully as possible the advantages and disadvantages of the two methods. [L]

4 A college of 3000 students has students registered in four departments, Arts, Science, Education and Crafts. The principal wishes to take a sample from the student population to gain information about likely student response to a

rearrangement of the college timetable so as to hold lectures on Wednesday, previously reserved for sports.
What sampling method would you advise the principal to use? Give reasons to justify your choice. [L]

5 Give the definition, practical implementation, advantages and disadvantages of stratified sampling.
A population of 15 values is stratified as follows

A	2	3	6	7	8
B	9	11	11	13	15
C	16	17	18	20	23

Explain why these strata are consistent with the stratification principle. [L]

6 In a survey of school children the variable measured was weight in kilograms. A random sample of 100 children had a mean weight of 37.2 kg and standard deviation of 3.6 kg
$\left(\text{i.e. } \sqrt{\left[\frac{\Sigma x^2}{n} - \bar{x}^2\right]} = 3.6\right)$.

(a) Find an unbiased estimate of the variance of the population from which this sample was taken.
(b) Find a 90% confidence interval for the mean weight.

A second sample of 100 children was taken and the mean weight was found to be 39.4 kg. The standard error of the difference in mean weights for the two samples was found to be 0.55 kg.

(c) Find a 95% confidence interval for the difference between the two means.
(d) Explain the importance of the fact that zero does not lie in this interval. [L]

7 The table below summarises the number of breakdowns on a stretch of motorway on 30 randomly selected days.

Number of breakdowns (x)	3	4	5	6	7	8	9	10	11
Number of days (f)	3	4	2	5	3	6	3	1	3

(a) Calculate unbiased estimates of the mean and the variance of the number of breakdowns.

Thirty more days were randomly sampled and this sample had a mean of 7.5 breakdowns and a standard deviation of 2.6 breakdowns (i.e. $s = 2.6$).

(b) Treating the 60 results as a single sample obtain further unbiased estimates of the population mean and the population variance.

(c) State, giving your reason, which of these two sets of estimates you would prefer to use. [L]

8 The number of errors per page made by a typesetter for a publisher has a Poisson distribution with mean 4.

Find, to 3 decimal places, the probability that

(a) on any page there are fewer than 4 errors,

(b) in a 2-page document there are more than 10 errors,

(c) on 2 consecutive pages, there are exactly 2 errors on each page.

A new typesetter is employed and the number of errors made by the typesetter in setting a page is counted.

(d) State appropriate null and alternative hypotheses to test that the new typesetter is at least as reliable as the other typesetter.

(e) Derive a critical region, of approximate size 0.05, to test the null hypothesis.

State the exact size of your critical region.

(f) A page of the work done by the new typesetter is selected at random and is found to contain 6 errors.

What conclusion can you draw from this value? [L]

[NB The size of a critical region is the probability of a type I error.]

9 The random variable X is normally distributed with mean μ and variance σ^2.

(a) Write down the distribution of the sample mean $\bar{X}$ of a random sample of size n.

An efficiency expert wishes to determine the mean time taken to drill a fixed number of holes in a metal sheet.

(b) Determine how large a random sample is needed so that the expert can be 95% certain that the sample mean time will differ from the true mean time by less than 15 seconds. Assume that it is known from previous studies that $\sigma = 40$ seconds. [L]

10 The machines in a factory produce an average of nine defective items each during a normal working day. As part of the factory management's search for greater efficiency they discover a new type of machine, which, it is claimed, will produce fewer defective items. They are offered a one-day trial on one of these machines to test whether the average number of defective items produced is lower. They also assume a Poisson distribution for the number of defective items produced by a single machine during a normal working day.

(a) State appropriate null and alternative hypotheses.

(b) Derive a critical region of size between 0.04 and 0.06 where the size of the critical region is defined as the probability that the alternative hypothesis is accepted given that the null hypothesis is true. State the exact size of the critical region.

(c) If six faulty items are produced by the new machine in the one-day trial, what conclusion should the factory management draw? [L]

[NB The size of a critical region is the probability of a type I error.]

11 The random variable X is normally distributed with mean μ and variance σ^2.

Write down the distribution of the sample mean $\bar{X}$ of a random sample of size n.

Explain what you understand by a 95% confidence interval.

A garage sells both leaded and unleaded petrol. The distribution of the values of sales for each type is normal. During 1990 the standard deviation of individual sales of each type of petrol is £3.25. The mean of the individual sales of leaded petrol during this time is £8.72.

A random sample of 100 individual sales of unleaded petrol gave a mean of £9.71.

Calculate

(a) an interval within which 90% of the sales of leaded petrol will lie

(b) a 95% confidence interval for the mean sales of unleaded petrol.

The mean of the sales of unleaded petrol for 1989 was £9.10. Using a 5% significance level, investigate whether there is sufficient evidence to conclude that the mean of all the 1990 unleaded sales was *greater* than the mean of the 1989 sales. Find the size of the sample that should be taken so that the garage proprietor can be 95% certain that the sample mean of sales of unleaded petrol during 1990 will differ from the true mean by less than 50p. [L]

12 Explain what is meant by a 98% confidence interval for a population mean.

The lengths, in cm, of the leaves of willow trees are known to be normally distributed with variance $1.33\,\text{cm}^2$. A sample of 40 willow tree leaves is found to have a mean of 10.20 cm.

(a) Estimate, giving your answer to 3 decimal places, the standard error of the mean. Use this value to estimate symmetrical 95% confidence limits for the mean length of the population of willow tree leaves, giving your answer to 2 decimal places.

(b) Find the minimum size of the sample of leaves which must be taken if the width of the symmetrical 98% confidence interval for the population mean is at most 1.50 cm. [L]

13 State the conditions under which a Poisson distribution with parameter μ can be approximated by a normal distribution. State the mean and variance of the approximate distribution.

The average number of lorries pulling into a motorway service station is 3 every 5 minutes.

(a) Explain why a Poisson distribution is suitable to model the number of lorries pulling into the service station per minute.

(b) Find, to 3 decimal places, the probability that in 10 minutes more than 7 lorries will pull into that service station.

(c) Estimate, giving your answer to 2 significant figures, the probability that more than 45 lorries will pull in during any one hour.

(d) When roadworks are started at the approach to the service station, the manager notices that during the next 4 hours only 100 lorries pull in. Assuming a Poisson model is still appropriate, perform a significance test at the 5% level to decide whether or not the average number of lorries pulling into the service station per hour has been reduced.

(e) Comment on the suitability of a Poisson model in (d).

[L]

14 Describe the roles of the null and alternative hypotheses in a test of significance. Explain how to decide whether the use of a one-tail or a two-tail test is appropriate.

Over a long period it has been found that the ratio of females to males attending classical ballet performances is 13 females to 7 males.

(a) On the afternoon of a football cup match, a random sample of 20 people attending a classical ballet performance is found to contain 4 males. Carry out a significance test to determine whether or not the proportion of males attending is lower than usual. State clearly your null and alternative hypotheses, and use a 10% significance level.

(b) At a contemporary ballet performance, a random sample of 100 people attending is found to contain 44 males. Set up null and alternative hypotheses and test whether or not the mean number of males attending contemporary ballet performances is different from that associated with clasical ballet performances. Use a normal approximation and a 5% level of significance. [L]

15 A normal population has variance 25. Find the size of the smallest sample which could be taken from the population so that the symmetrical 90% confidence interval for the population mean has width less than 3 units.

16 The distance driven by a long distance lorry driver in a week is a normally distributed variable having mean 1130 km and standard deviation 106 km. Find, to 3 decimal places, the probability that in a given week he will drive less than 1000 km.

Find, to 3 decimal places, the probability that in 20 weeks his average distance driven per week is more than 1200 km.

New driving regulations are introduced and, in the first 20 weeks after their introduction, he drives a total of 21 900 km. Assuming that the standard deviation of the weekly distances he drives is unchanged, test, at the 10% level of significance, whether his mean weekly driving distance has been reduced. State clearly your null and alternative hypotheses. [L]

17 Climbing rope produced by a manufacturer is known to be such that one-metre lengths have breaking strengths that are normally distributed with mean 170.2 kg and standard deviation 10.5 kg. Find, to 3 decimal places, the probability that

(a) a one-metre length of rope chosen at random from those produced by the manufacturer will have a breaking strength of 175 kg to the nearest kg.

(b) a random sample of 50 one-metre lengths will have a mean breaking strength of more than 172.4 kg.

A new component material is added to the ropes being produced. The manufacturer believes that this will increase the mean breaking strength without changing the standard deviation. A random sample of 50 one-metre lengths of the new rope is found to have a mean breaking strength of 172.4 kg. Perform a significance test at the 5% level to decide whether this result provides sufficient evidence to confirm the manufacturer's belief that the mean breaking strength is increased. State clearly the null and alternative hypotheses which you are using. [L]

18 Sketch the distribution N(0,1).
Given an example of data that you have met which may be approximately modelled by a normal distribution.
Explain what is meant by a 98% confidence interval for a population mean.
A machine fills '1 kg' packets of sugar. The actual weight of sugar delivered to each packet may be assumed to be normally distributed. The manufacturer requires that
(a) the mean weight of the contents of a packet is 1010 g, and
(b) 95% of all packets filled by the machine contain between 1000 g and 1020 g of sugar.
Show that this is equivalent to demanding that the variance of the sampling distribution, to 2 decimal places, is equal to 26.03 g^2.
A sample of 8 packets was selected at random from those filled by the machine. The weights, in grams, of the contents of these packets were

1012.6 1017.7 1015.2 1015.7 1020.9 1005.7 1009.9 1011.4

Assuming that the variance of the actual weights is 26.03 g^2, perform a significance test at the 2% significance level, stating clearly the null and alternative hypotheses that you are using, to decide whether this sample provides sufficient evidence to conclude that the machine is *not* fulfilling condition (a). [L]

19 (i) Write down the mean and the variance of the distribution of the means of all possible samples of size n taken from an infinite population having mean μ and variance σ^2.
Describe the form of this distribution of sample means when
(a) n is large
(b) the distribution of the population is normal.
(ii) The standard deviation of all the till receipts of a supermarket during 1984 was £4.25.
(a) Given that the mean of a random sample of 100 of the till receipts is £18.50, obtain an approximate 95% confidence interval for the mean of all the till receipts during 1984.

(b) Find the size of sample that should be taken so that the management can be 95% confident that the sample mean will not differ from the true mean by more than 50p.

(c) The mean of all the till receipts of the supermarket during 1983 was £19.40. Using a 5% significance level, investigate whether the sample in (a) above provides sufficient evidence to conclude that the mean of all the 1984 till receipts is different from that in 1983. [L]

20 Records of the diameters of spherical ball bearings produced on a certain machine indicate that the diameters are Normally distributed with mean 0.824 cm and standard deviation 0.046 cm. Two hundred samples, each consisting of 100 ball bearings, are chosen. Calculate the expected number of the 200 samples having a mean diameter less than 0.823 cm.
On a certain day it was suspected that the machine was malfunctioning. It may be assumed that if the machine is malfunctioning it will change the mean of the diameters without changing their standard deviation. On that day a random sample of 100 ball bearing had a mean diameter of 0.834 cm. Determine a 98% confidence interval for the mean diameter of the ball bearings being produced that day.
Hence state whether or not you would conclude that the machine is malfunctioning on that day given that the significance level is 2%. [L]

21 (a) The diameters of eggs of the little gull are approximately normally distributed with mean 4.11 cm and standard deviation 0.19 cm. Calculate the probability that an egg chosen at random has a diameter between 3.9 cm and 4.5 cm.

A sample of 8 little gull eggs was collected from a particular island and their diameters, in cm, were

4.4, 4.5, 4.1, 3.9, 4.4, 4.6, 4.5, 4.1

Assuming that the standard deviation of the diameters of eggs from the island is also 0.19 cm, investigate, at the 1% level, whether the results indicate that the mean diameter of little gull eggs on this island is different from elsewhere.

If you conclude that there is a difference, state the direction of this difference.

(b) During the 7 years from 1950 to 1956 inclusive, electric traction was used on 2500 miles of railway line. During these years, 35 child trespassers were fatally electrocuted. In a succeeding year, 3 children were fatally electrocuted on one 100 mile stretch of the line in separate incidents. Assuming that the numbers of children fatally electrocuted have Poisson distributions, investigate whether this stretch of line requires additional protection. [L]

Correlation

3

3.1 Correlation

There are many situations where we are interested in the relationship between two random variables such as the height and weight of people, or the marks a person attained in Mathematics and the mark they attained in Physics. A pair of observations from two such variables is called a **bi-variate distribution**.

While you might expect there to be a relationship between Mathematics and Physics marks, you cannot expect to find a law relating them. You can only look for the most basic of relationships, such as:
Does a higher than average Mathematics mark usually go with a higher than average Physics mark, or does a higher than average Mathematics mark go with a lower than average Physics mark?

The technique used to measure the degree of linear relationship between two variables is called **linear correlation**. If both variables increase together we say that they are **positively correlated**. For example, height and weight of people might be positively correlated. If one variable increases as the other decreases then they are said to be **negatively correlated**. For example, the number of goals conceded by a team and their position in the league might be negatively correlated. If the points are scattered so that no pattern can be seen then there is said to be no correlation between the variables. For example, there is no correlation between a person's height and the amount they earn.

Scatter diagrams

The association between the two variables may be seen by plotting the pairs of observations on a graph. The graph is known as a **scatter diagram** since it enables you to see how the pairs of points are scattered.

These scatter diagrams show possible relationships:

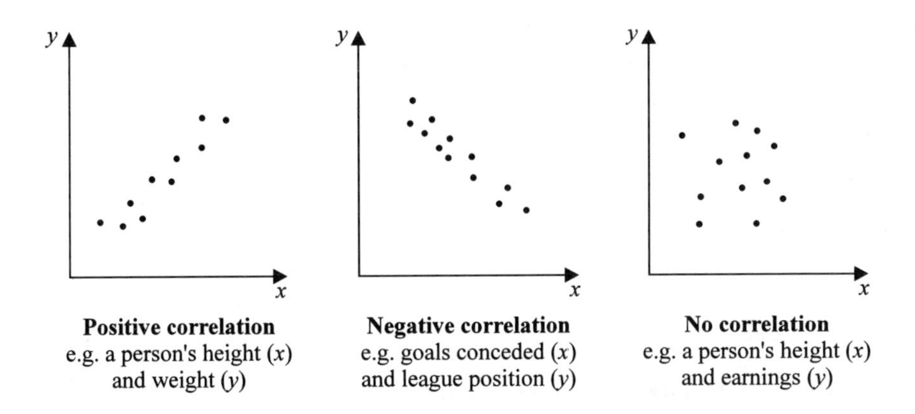

If a horizontal line is drawn through the mean y value, $\bar{y}$, and a vertical line through the mean x value, $\bar{x}$, and if you move the axes to these two lines, you can see the relationship between the two variables in another way.

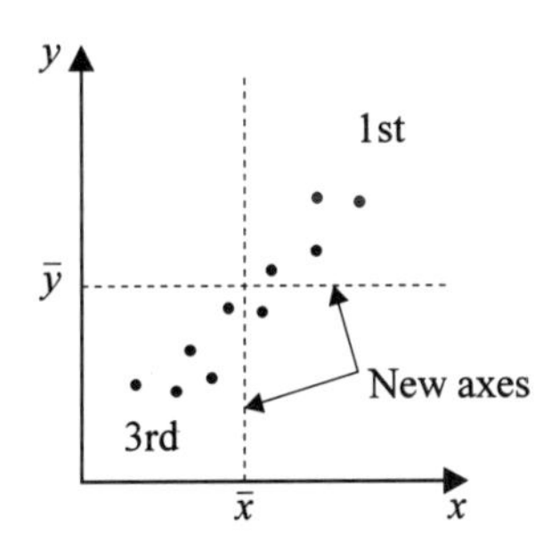

For a positive correlation most points lie in the first and third quadrants.

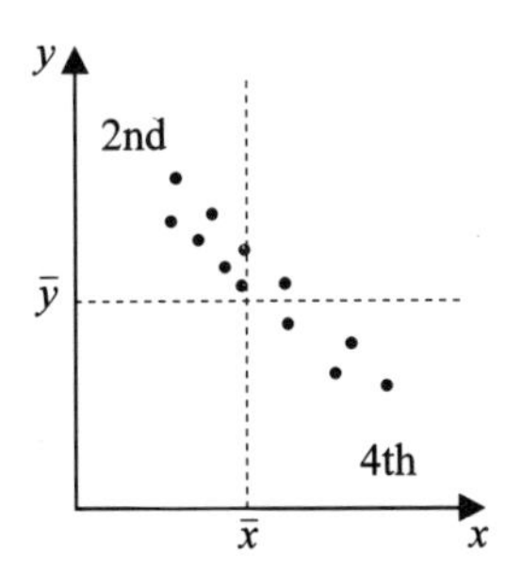

For a negative correlation most points lie in the second and fourth quadrants.

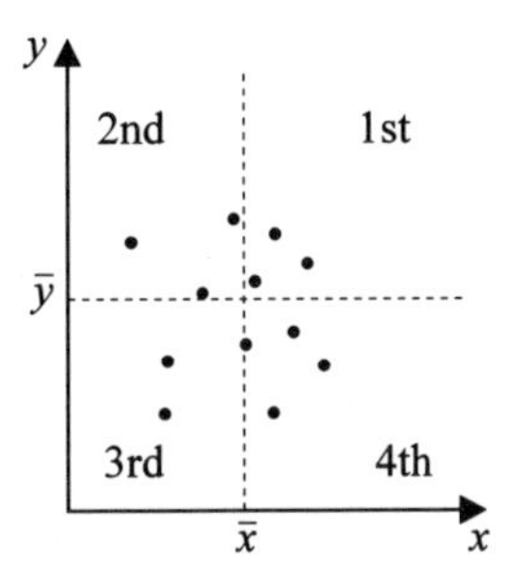

Example 1

The weight (kg), head size (circumference in cm) and gestation period (weeks) of new-born male babies at a certain clinic over a period of time was as follows.

Baby	A	B	C	D	E	F	G	H	I	J
Weight w (kg)	3.10	3.24	3.15	3.30	3.12	3.41	3.52	3.40	3.53	3.74
Head size h (cm)	31.1	33.3	30.0	31.5	35.0	30.2	36.4	37.3	31.4	34.0
Gestation period p (weeks)	36	37	38	38	40	40	40	41	41	41

It is thought that head size h and weight w may be correlated, and that the gestation period p and weight w might also be correlated.

Plot scatter diagrams and state whether there is evidence to support these conjectures. If there is, state whether the correlation is positive or negative. (You may use $\bar{w} = 3.35$, $\bar{h} = 33.02$, $\bar{p} = 39.2$.)

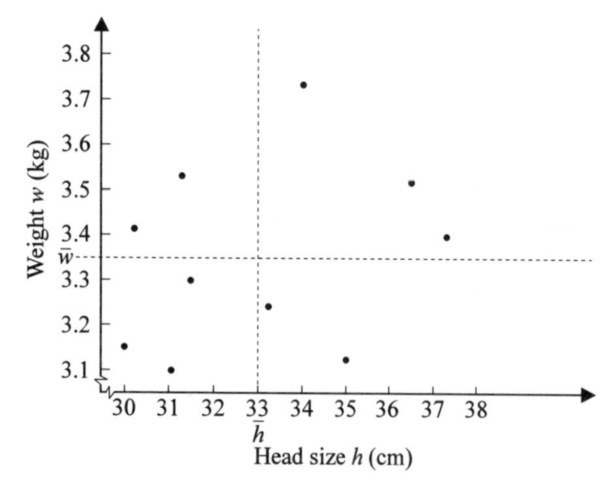

Scatter diagram of weight w (kg) and head size h (cm)

Points are fairly evenly scattered in all four quadrants so there is no evidence of a correlation between head size h and weight w.

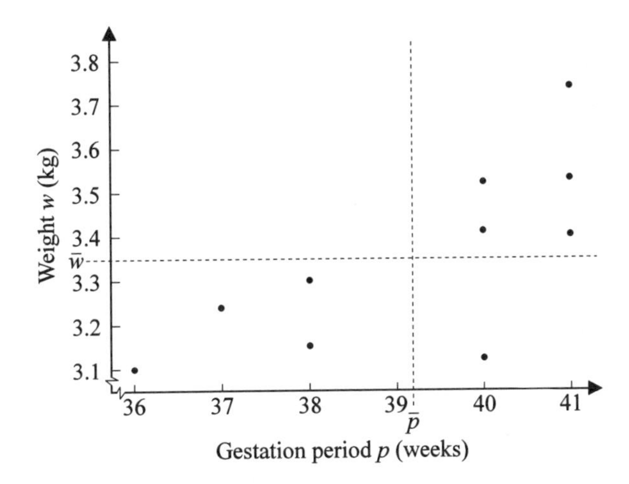

Scatter diagram of gestation period (p) weeks and weight (kg)

Since most of the points of the scatter diagrams lie in the first and third quadrants there is a positive correlation between weight w and gestation period p. As gestation period increases weight increases.

Example 2

In the study of a city, the population density p (people/hectare), and the distance from the city centre d (km) was investigated by picking a number of sample areas with the following results.

Area	A	B	C	D	E	F	G	H	I	J
Distance, d (km)	0.6	3.8	2.4	3.0	2.0	1.5	1.8	3.4	4.0	0.9
Population density, p (people/hectare)	50	22	14	20	33	47	25	8	16	38

Plot a scatter diagram and by plotting the mean values of d and p suggest what type of correlation is present.

$$\bar{d} = \frac{\Sigma d}{n} = 2.34$$

$$\bar{p} = \frac{\Sigma p}{n} = 27.3$$

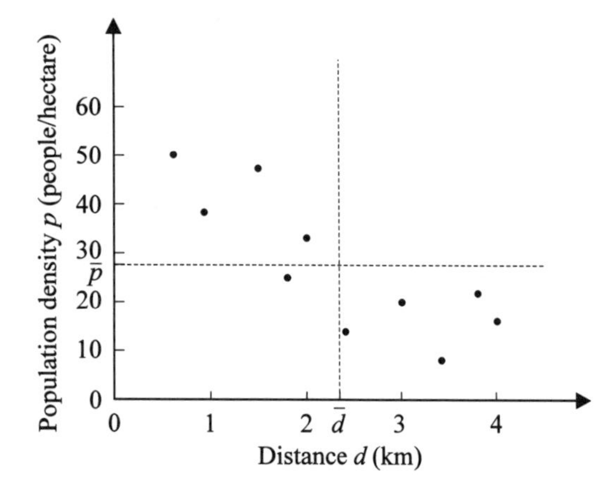

Scatter diagram of population density p and distance d

Most points lie in the second and fourth quadrants, so the population density p and distance from the city centre d are negatively correlated. As distance increases the population density decreases.

3.2 Product-moment correlation coefficient (PMCC)

You can see from a scatter diagram whether two variables are correlated, but you have no measure of how *strong* this relationship is. The diagram below shows a typical scatter diagram for a bi-variate distribution with the n pairs of observations of the two variables x and y plotted.

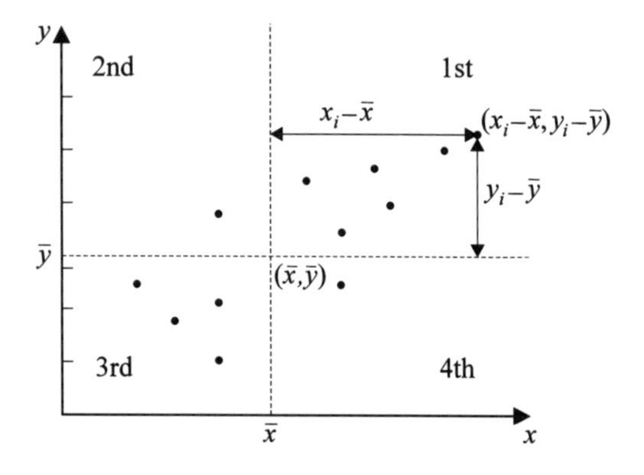

Scatter diagram for x and y

To show up any relationship more clearly, you can move the origin of the diagram to the point $(\bar{x}, \bar{y})$. The coordinate of a typical point (x_i, y_i) will now be written as $(x_i - \bar{x}, y_i - \bar{y})$. The ith point on the diagram has been labelled to show this.

If you look at the scatter diagram you can see the signs (+ or −) taken by all the $x_i - \bar{x}$ and $y_i - \bar{y}$ in the four new quadrants. By multiplying the signs, you can find the sign taken by their product $(x_i - \bar{x})(y_i - \bar{y})$.

Quadrant	$x_i - \bar{x}$	$y_i - \bar{y}$	$(x_i - \bar{x})(y_i - \bar{y})$
first	+	+	+
second	−	+	−
third	−	−	+
fourth	+	−	−

Now think about the three types of correlation:

If there is a **positive correlation**, most points lie in the first and third quadrants so $\Sigma(x_i-\bar{x})(y_i-\bar{y})$ **would be positive**.

If there is a **negative correlation**, most points lie in the second and fourth quadrants so $\Sigma(x_i-\bar{x})(y_i-\bar{y})$ **would be negative**.

If there is **no correlation** the points lie in all four quadrants and $\Sigma(x_i-\bar{x})(y_i-\bar{y})$ **is zero or close to zero**, since the positive and negative values tend to cancel out.

You can now see why we call a correlation positive or negative.

The numerical value of $\Sigma(x_i - \bar{x})(y_i - \bar{y})$ will depend on the units of measurement. To see this, think about a simple calculation of area. If you measure the area of a rectangle 10 mm by 12 mm in square millimetres the area will be $10 \times 12 = 120\,\text{mm}^2$. If you measure the same shape in centimetres the area will be $1 \times 1.2 = 1.2\,\text{cm}^2$. In the same way the numerical value of each $(x_i - \bar{x})(y_i - \bar{y})$ will depend on the units of measurement.

The numerical value of $\sum_{i=1}^{n}(x_i - \bar{x})(y_i - \bar{y})$ will also depend on how many values are added together, i.e. the value of n.

A more useful measure of correlation would be one that is independent of the sample size and the scales of measurement used. You can allow for the sample size by dividing by n to find the mean value of $(x_i - \bar{x})(y_i - \bar{y})$. This may be written

$$\frac{1}{n}\sum(x_i - \bar{x})(y_i - \bar{y})$$

To allow for different scales of measurement you can use the same idea as you did when standardising the normal distribution in Book T1 (chapter 8). There, you may recall, you standardised the normal distribution by dividing the deviation from the mean by the standard deviation. Since here you are dealing with a sample from a bi-variate distribution, you divide by

$$\sqrt{\frac{\sum(x_i - \bar{x})^2}{n}}\sqrt{\frac{\sum(y_i - \bar{y})^2}{n}}$$

The standardised measure now becomes:

$$\frac{\frac{1}{n}\sum(x_i - \bar{x})(y_i - \bar{y})}{\sqrt{\left(\frac{\sum(x_i - \bar{x})^2}{n}\right)}\sqrt{\left(\frac{\sum(y_i - \bar{y})^2}{n}\right)}} = \frac{\sum(x_i - \bar{x})(y_i - \bar{y})}{\sqrt{(\sum(x_i - \bar{x})^2)}\sqrt{(\sum(y_i - \bar{y})^2)}}$$

This measure is known as the **product-moment correlation coefficient** r.

For short, we normally denote $\sum(x_i - \bar{x})(y_i - \bar{y})$ by S_{xy}. So:

- $\boldsymbol{S_{xy} = \sum(x_i - \bar{x})(y_i - \bar{y})}$

and in a similar way we write:

- $\boldsymbol{S_{xx} = \sum(x_i - \bar{x})^2}$

and

- $\boldsymbol{S_{yy} = \sum(y_i - \bar{y})^2}$

- **Product-moment correlation coefficient**

$$\boldsymbol{r = \frac{S_{xy}}{\sqrt{(S_{xx}S_{yy})}} = \frac{\sum(x_i - \bar{x})(y_i - \bar{y})}{\sqrt{(\sum(x_i - \bar{x})^2(y_i - \bar{y})^2)}}}$$

Summations of the form $\sum(x_i - \bar{x})^p(y_i - \bar{y})^q$ are known as product-moments about the mean. The one we are interested in is of low order, with $p = q = 1$. (The other ones will not be of concern to you.) This explains why the standardised measure is called the product-moment correlation coefficient. Because of the standardisation, the measure can be shown to lie in the interval -1 to $+1$, and it gives us a measure of the strength of the relationship between the two variables.

Example 3

The mean points scored in the GCSE and the mean points scored at A-level by pupils of a sample of schools from a particular county were:

School	A	B	C	D	E	F	G	H	I	J	K	L	M	N	O
A-level (x)	8.6	13.4	12.8	9.3	1.3	9.4	13.1	4.9	13.5	9.6	7.5	9.8	23.3	21	19.4
GCSE (y)	33	51	30	48	12	23	46	18	36	50	34	35	95	99	69

(a) Draw a scatter diagram of these results.
(b) Calculate the product-moment correlation coefficient for GCSE and A-level scores.

(a)

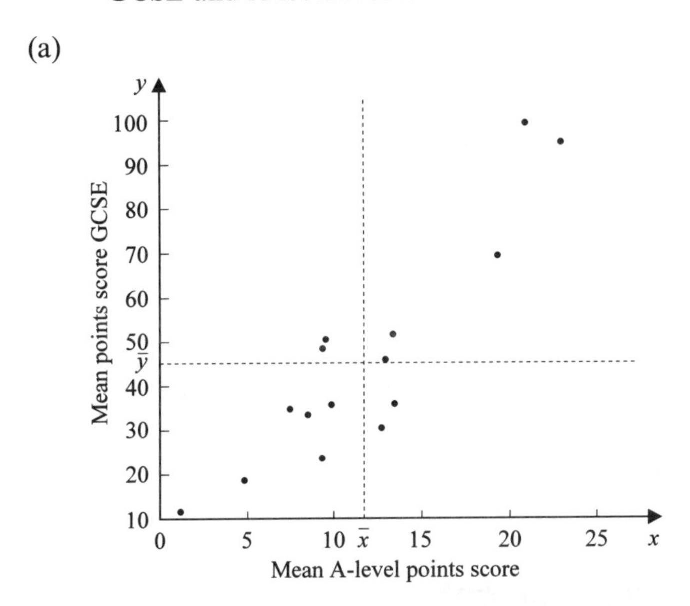

Scatter diagram of A level and GCSE points

(b) The mean values of x and y are:

$$\bar{y} = 45.27 \qquad \bar{x} = 11.80$$

x	y	$x-\bar{x}$	$y-\bar{y}$	$(x-\bar{x})^2$	$(y-\bar{y})^2$	$(x-\bar{x})(y-\bar{y})$
8.6	33	−3.2	−12.27	10.24	150.55	39.26
13.4	51	1.6	5.73	2.56	32.83	9.17
12.8	30	1	−15.27	1.00	233.17	−15.27
9.3	48	−2.5	2.73	6.25	7.45	−6.83
1.3	12	−10.5	−33.27	110.25	1106.89	349.34
9.4	23	−2.4	−22.27	5.76	495.95	53.45
13.1	46	1.3	0.73	1.69	0.53	0.95
4.9	18	−6.9	−27.27	47.61	743.65	188.16
13.5	36	1.7	−9.27	2.89	85.93	−15.76
9.6	50	−2.2	4.73	4.84	22.37	−10.41
7.5	34	−4.3	−11.27	18.49	127.01	48.46
9.8	35	−2	−10.27	4.00	105.47	20.54
23.3	95	11.5	49.73	132.25	2473.07	571.90
21.0	99	9.2	53.73	84.64	2886.91	494.32
19.4	69	7.6	23.73	57.76	563.11	180.35
				$S_{xx} = 490.23$	$S_{yy} = 9034.89$	$S_{xy} = 1907.63$

The product-moment correlation coefficient is:

$$r = \frac{S_{xy}}{\sqrt{(S_{xx}S_{yy})}} = \frac{\sum(x_i-\bar{x})(y_i-\bar{y})}{\sqrt{\sum(x_i-\bar{x})^2(y_i-\bar{y})^2}}$$

$$= \frac{1907.63}{\sqrt{(490.23 \times 9034.89)}}$$

$$= 0.906$$

A quicker way of finding the product-moment correlation coefficient *r*

By means of some algebraic manipulation of S_{xy}, S_{xx} and S_{yy} you can find another formula that can save you a lot of calculation time.

$$S_{xy} = \sum(x_i-\bar{x})(y_i-\bar{y})$$

$$= \sum(x_iy_i - \bar{x}y_i - \bar{y}x_i + \bar{x}\bar{y}) \qquad \text{(multiply out the brackets)}$$

$$= \sum x_iy_i - \sum \bar{x}y_i - \sum \bar{y}x_i + \sum \bar{x}\bar{y} \qquad \text{(sum the individual parts)}$$

$$= \sum x_iy_i - \bar{x}\sum y_i - \bar{y}\sum x_i + n\bar{x}\bar{y} \qquad \text{(since } \bar{x} \text{ and } \bar{y} \text{ are constants)}$$

$$= \sum x_iy_i - \frac{\sum x_i}{n}\sum y_i - \frac{\sum y_i}{n}\sum x_i + n\frac{\sum x_i}{n}\frac{\sum y_i}{n} \qquad \left(\bar{x} = \frac{\sum x_i}{n} \text{ and } \bar{y} = \frac{\sum y_i}{n}\right)$$

$$= \sum x_iy_i - \frac{\sum x_i \sum y_i}{n}$$

If you treat S_{xx} and S_{yy} in a similar way you get:

$$S_{xx} = \sum x_i^2 - \frac{(\sum x_i)^2}{n}$$

$$S_{yy} = \sum y_i^2 - \frac{(\sum y_i)^2}{n}$$

You need to be able to use these formulae in the product-moment correlation coefficient calculations, as it saves time. Both forms are given in the London Examination Board's booklet of mathematical formulae. Using these gives:

- $r = \dfrac{S_{xy}}{\sqrt{(S_{xx}S_{yy})}}$

- $r = \dfrac{\sum x_i y_i - \dfrac{\sum x_i \sum y_i}{n}}{\sqrt{\left[\left(\sum x_i^2 - \dfrac{(\sum x_i)^2}{n}\right)\left(\sum y_i^2 - \dfrac{(\sum y_i)^2}{n}\right)\right]}}$

Of the two equations for r, the first is more suitable for understanding the theoretical basis of the product-moment correlation coefficient and the second is more suitable for calculating it. It is also possible to obtain statistical calculators which, when you feed in the pairs of values, do all the calculations for you and give a value for r. If you have one of these you can check that you can use your calculator correctly by doing example 3.

Example 4

Using the figures from example 3 calculate the PMCC using the formula more suited to calculation.

x	y	x^2	y^2	xy
8.6	33	73.96	1809	283.8
13.4	51	179.56	2601	683.4
12.8	30	163.84	900	384
9.3	48	86.49	2304	446.4
1.3	12	1.69	144	15.6
9.4	23	88.36	529	216.2
13.1	46	171.61	2116	602.6
4.9	18	24.01	324	88.2
13.5	36	182.25	1296	486
9.6	50	92.16	2500	480
7.5	34	56.25	1156	255
9.8	35	96.04	1225	343
23.3	95	542.89	9025	2213.5
21	99	441	9801	2079
19.4	69	376.36	4761	1338.6
$\sum x = 176.9$	$\sum y = 679$	$\sum x^2 = 2576.47$	$\sum y^2 = 39\,771$	$\sum xy = 9915.3$

$$r = \frac{S_{xy}}{\sqrt{(S_{xx}S_{yy})}} = \frac{\sum x_i y_i - \dfrac{\sum x_i \sum y_i}{n}}{\sqrt{\left[\left(\sum x_i^2 - \dfrac{(\sum x_i)^2}{n}\right)\left(\sum y_i^2 - \dfrac{(\sum y_i)^2}{n}\right)\right]}}$$

$$= \frac{9915.3 - \dfrac{176.9 \times 679}{15}}{\sqrt{\left[\left(2576.47 - \dfrac{176.9^2}{15}\right)\left(39\,771 - \dfrac{679^2}{15}\right)\right]}}$$

$$= \frac{1907.63}{\sqrt{(490.23 \times 9034.93)}}$$

$$= 0.906 \ldots$$

If you use a statistical calculator it may give you the value of the product-moment correlation coefficient. To just write down the answer is risky since no marks will be given if it is incorrect. It is also possible that you may be asked to find intermediate values in the calculation such as S_{xx}, S_{yy}, etc., as well as the value of r. It is not necessary to draw up a table. A good layout for the above question might be as follows:

$$\sum x = 176.9 \quad \sum y = 679 \quad \sum x^2 = 2576.47 \quad \sum y^2 = 39\,771$$

$$\sum xy = 9915.3$$

$$S_{xx} = 2576.47 - \frac{176.9^2}{15} = 490.23$$

$$S_{yy} = 39\,771 - \frac{679^2}{15} = 9034.93$$

$$S_{xy} = 9915.3 - \frac{176.9 \times 679}{15} = 1907.63$$

$$r = \frac{S_{xy}}{\sqrt{(S_{xx}S_{yy})}} = \frac{1907.63}{\sqrt{(490.23 \times 9034.93)}}$$

$$r = 0.906 \ldots$$

Using a method of coding

You can further simplify the calculations by making the numbers you use for the values of x and y smaller. You can subtract any number from the x values, since this only moves the axis. You can divide the result by any number, since this only changes the scale. The correlation coefficient is unaffected by either of these operations. The number you subtract and divided by can be selected in any way you choose, but it is common sense to make their values such that the resulting numbers are small. You can rewrite the variables x and y as

$$X = \frac{x - a}{b} \quad \text{and} \quad Y = \frac{y - c}{d}$$

where a, b, c and d are suitable numbers to be chosen. The next example illustrates this method.

Example 5

Use the method of coding to find the product-moment correlation coefficient for x and y if the values of x and y are as shown in the table below. Draw a scatter diagram of the new values.

x	1020	1032	1028	1034	1023	1038
y	320	335	345	355	360	380

You can use the coding:

$$X = \frac{x - 1020}{1} \qquad Y = \frac{y - 300}{5}$$

Here $a = 1020$ and $b = 1$. These were chosen because 1020 was the smallest x value and the numbers then left had no common divisor. In the same way $c = 300$ and $d = 5$ since the numbers that are left have 5 as a common divisor. (We could have used 320 and made the values even smaller, but wished to show that *any* number will do the job.)

X	Y	X^2	Y^2	XY
0	4	0	16	0
12	7	144	49	84
8	9	64	81	72
14	11	196	121	154
3	12	9	144	36
18	16	324	256	288
$\sum X = 55$	$\sum Y = 59$	$\sum X^2 = 737$	$\sum Y^2 = 667$	$\sum XY = 634$

$$r = \frac{S_{xy}}{\sqrt{(S_{xx}S_{yy})}} = \frac{\sum X_iY_i - \frac{\sum X_i \sum Y_i}{n}}{\sqrt{\left[\left(\sum X_i^2 - \frac{(\sum X_i)^2}{n}\right)\left(\sum Y_i^2 - \frac{(\sum Y_i)^2}{n}\right)\right]}}$$

$$= \frac{634 - \frac{55 \times 59}{6}}{\sqrt{\left[\left(737 - \frac{55^2}{6}\right)\left(667 - \frac{59^2}{6}\right)\right]}}$$

$$= \frac{93.17}{142.19}$$

$$= 0.655$$

Here is the scatter diagram of the new values:

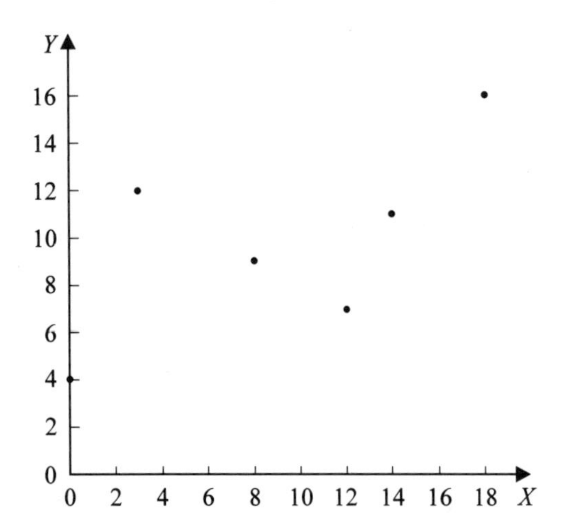

Scatter diagram for X and Y

Interpreting the product-moment correlation coefficient

In examples 3 and 4 we found the value of the product-moment coefficient by using two different formulae. But what does a value of r actually tell you?

For values of r between 0 and 1, the nearer the value of r is to 1 the stronger the positive association between the two variables. If you look at example 3 you can see what a fairly strong positive correlation ($r = 0.906$) looks like on a scatter diagram. In example 5 ($r = 0.6555$) you can see what a weaker one looks like.

For values between -1 and 0, the closer the value of r gets to -1 the stronger the negative correlation.

It is always a good idea to plot a scatter diagram, as this gives you a picture of the correlation, and also helps to identify any results that are well away from the other points and so do not fit the general pattern of any correlation shown up by the diagram. These are known as **rogue results**. A rogue result may sometimes be called an **outlier** and may have occurred in a number of ways – for example, a value may have been misread or a child was ill during a test and underperformed thus upsetting the general trend. A proper study of this topic is beyond the scope of this book; it is dealt with in the T3 syllabus.

- **If $r = 1$ there is a perfect positive linear correlation between the two variables (all points fit a straight line with positive gradient).**
- **If $r = -1$ there is a perfect negative linear correlation between the two variables (all points fit a straight line with negative gradient).**
- **If r is zero (or close to zero) there is no linear correlation; this does not, however, exclude any other sort of relationship.**

These cases are illustrated below:

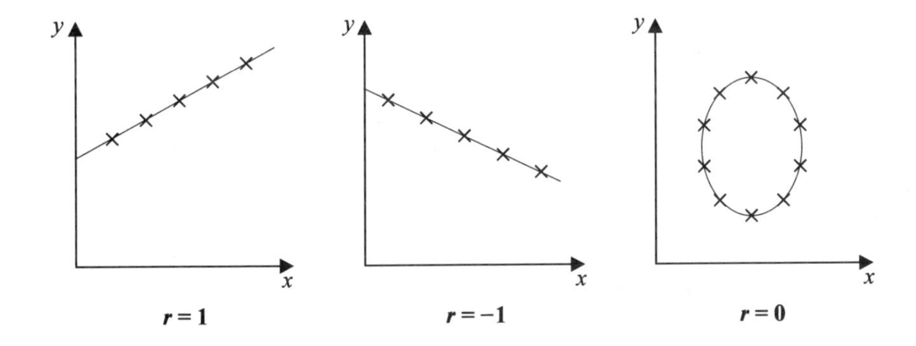

Because two variables have a linear correlation (positive or negative) it does not necessarily mean they are related. For example, there may be a correlation between the number of cars on the road and the number of television sets bought, but this does not mean that the two are related. So you should have some reason to believe that there might be a relationship before calculating the product-moment correlation coefficient, unless your aim is to prove that they are unrelated.

Often variables are linked only through a third variable. A good example of this is changes that take place over time. For example, over the past ten years the memory capacity of personal computers has increased, and so has the average life expectancy of people in the western world. The two are not connected, but both are due to scientific development over time.

There is little point in comparing two variables if one of them forms a part of the other. You would expect your statistics project mark to compare to your overall course mark, since it forms part of that assessment. From the correlation point of view, what perhaps you should look at is the correlation between your project mark and that obtained in your written examination.

Testing the hypothesis that a population product-moment correlation coefficient is zero

We have said that if a product-moment correlation coefficient is zero, or near zero, the two variables are not associated. We say 'near zero' because our sets of data are samples from a population, and each time we take a sample we would get a different value of the product-moment correlation coefficient r. But how near must the value of r be to zero before you can say there is zero correlation? We cannot in general answer this question, but if both variables X and Y are normally distributed, and if for each value of one variable, the values of the other variable are normally distributed, and vice versa, then we *can* do so. This is quite a difficult situation to picture, but an example might help.

If X is the lengths of leaves taken from a tree and Y is the widths of the leaves from the tree then you would expect X to be normally distributed and you would expect Y to be normally distributed. If you now take a particular length of leaf, the widths of all the leaves of this length will be normally distributed, and if you take a particular width, the lengths of all leaves having this width would be normally distributed. When two variables are related in this way they are said to be **jointly normally distributed**, so leaf length and leaf width are jointly normally distributed. If you assume that the random variables X and Y are jointly normally distributed and that they have a correlation coefficient ρ (rho) and that data are collected so that there is a random sample from all the values of X and Y, then the mean value of all the product-moment coefficients found from all possible samples will be ρ. In other words, r is an unbiased estimator of ρ. In practical terms, you can assume that X and Y are jointly normally distributed provided both are variables with continuous measures which could separately be assumed to be normal, and provided that the points on the scatter diagram lie within an elliptical shape. If these conditions are not met it is still possible to do a test but you have to use a rank correlation coefficient. You will be looking at one of these later in the chapter.

If you plot the probability distribution function $f(r)$ for the product-moment correlation coefficient r when the variables are jointly normally distributed and have a population product-moment correlation coefficient $\rho = 0$, then you get a probability distribution diagram symmetrical about $r = 0$ as shown below.

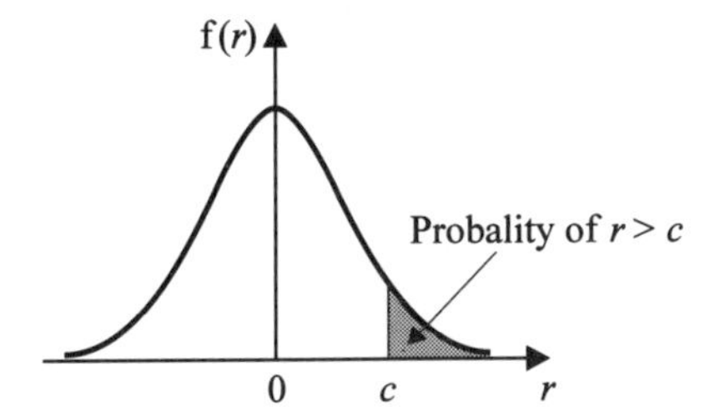

As is usual with these diagrams, the probability that r exceeds any given value c is given by the area under the graph to the right of c, and the probability of getting a value of r less than c is given by the area to the left of c.

We are usually interested in a value of c which r exceeds with a small probability. We call this the *critical value* of r at the probability level chosen. Typical probability levels are 0.1, 0.05, 0.025, 0.01 and 0.005 (10%, 5%, 2.5%, 1% and 0.5%). The critical value will depend upon the probability level chosen, and also upon the number of observations (n). Table 6 on page 209 gives critical values of r (one-tailed test) for each of these probability levels for different values of n.

If you think there is no correlation, you set up a null hypothesis H_0: $\rho = 0$. (The population product-moment correlation coefficient = 0.) You then decide the probability that you are willing to accept of being wrong if you reject the null hypothesis when it is correct (the significance level), and test to see if the value of the sample product-moment correlation coefficient r gives evidence to suggest that $\rho = 0$.

From the table you see that if $\rho = 0$, for a sampling size of 10, the critical value of r which is significant at the 0.05 level (5%) on a one-tailed test is 0.5494.

If you use as your alternative hypothesis H_1: $\rho \neq 0$ then you would use a two-tailed test. The critical values of r are ± 0.6319. The critical region at the 5% level for $n = 10$ would become $r < -0.6319$ or $r > 0.6319$, allowing $2\frac{1}{2}\%$ at each tail (0.025 level).

Example 6

By using $\sum x = 20$, $\sum y = 35$, $\sum xy = 65$, $\sum x^2 = 35$, $\sum y^2 = 130$, calculate the product-moment correlation between 20 pairs of readings. Using a 0.05 significance level, test the hypothesis that $\rho = 0$ (use a two-tailed test).

$$r = \frac{S_{xy}}{\sqrt{(S_{xx}S_{yy})}} = \frac{\sum x_i y_i - \frac{\sum x_i \sum y_i}{n}}{\sqrt{\left[\left(\sum x^2{}_i - \frac{(\sum x_i)^2}{n}\right)\left(\sum y^2{}_i - \frac{(\sum y_i)^2}{n}\right)\right]}}$$

$$= \frac{65 - \frac{20 \times 35}{20}}{\sqrt{\left[\left(35 - \frac{20^2}{20}\right)\left(130 - \frac{35^2}{120}\right)\right]}}$$

$$= 0.934 \ldots$$

H_0: $\rho = 0$ There is zero correlation between the readings.
H_1: $\rho \neq 0$ (two-tailed) There is either a positive or a negative correlation.

From Table 6 the critical values of r are ± 0.4438 and the critical region is $r < -0.4438$ or $r > 0.4438$.

The result is significant at the 0.05 level.
You reject H_0: the correlation is not zero.

Example 7
The product-moment correlation coefficient between 30 pairs of reactions is $r = -0.45$. Use a 0.05 significance level and a two-tailed test to test the hypothesis $\rho = 0$.

H_0: $\rho = 0$ There is zero correlation between the readings.
H_1: $\rho \neq 0$ (two-tailed) There is either a positive or a negative correlation.

From Table 6 the critical values of r are ± 0.3610 and the critical region is $r < -0.3610$ and $r > 0.3610$.

Since $r = -0.45$ it is significant at the 0.05 level.
You reject H_0 and accept H_1: $\rho \neq 0$. There is some correlation.

Example 8
For 8 pairs of observations the product-moment correlation coefficient is $r = 0.667$. Does this value indicate

(a) a correlation significantly different to zero at the 5% level
(b) a significant positive correlation at the 5% level?

(a) H_0: $\rho = 0$ There is zero correlation between the readings.
H_1: $\rho \neq 0$ (two-tailed test) There is either a positive or a negative correlation.

From Table 6 for a sample size of 8 the critical values are ± 0.7067. The critical region is $r < -0.7067$ and $r > 0.7067$.

Since $r = 0.667$ it is not significant at the 5% level.
You do not reject H_0: $\rho = 0$. There is no evidence to show that the correlation is significantly different to zero.

(b) H_0: $\rho = 0$ There is zero correlation between the readings.
H_1: $\rho > 0$ (one-tailed test) There is a positive correlation.

From Table 6 for a sample size of 8 the critical value is 0.6215 and the critical region is $r > 0.6125$.

Since $r = 0.667$ it is significant at the 5% level.
You reject H_0. There is evidence of a positive correlation at the 5% level.

Exercise 3A

1 Find the product-moment correlation coefficient for each of the following sets of data.

(a) $\sum x_i = 367$, $\sum y_i = 270$, $\sum x_i^2 = 23845$, $\sum y_i^2 = 12976$, $\sum x_i y_i = 17135$, $n = 6$

(b) $\sum x_i = 357.7$, $\sum y_i = 278.7$, $\sum x_i^2 = 11696.95$, $\sum y_i^2 = 7119.71$, $\sum x_i y_i = 8396.1$, $n = 12$

(c) $\sum x_i = 22.09$, $\sum y_i = 49.7$, $\sum x_i^2 = 45.04$, $\sum y_i^2 = 244.83$, $\sum x_i y_i = 97.778$, $n = 12$

2 For each of the following data sets plot a scatter diagram, and then calculate the product-moment correlation coefficient.

(a)

x	1	2.3	3.6	2.1	4.8	3.1	4	0.5
y	6.2	9.1	16.8	7	19.3	12.4	16	3.8

(b)

x	125	159	285	210	152	243	279	116	181	162	236
y	75	70	54	63	68	56	50	77	68	73	56

3 Use a method of coding to calculate the product-moment correlation coefficient for each of the following sets of data.

(a)

x	1503	1508	1517	1511	1520
y	45.2	55.1	60.2	58.3	65

(b)

x	297.1	286.4	290.2	288.4	293.1	300
y	43.2	48.7	46.1	47.2	46.1	41

(c)

x	0.0015	0.0018	0.0013	0.0016	0.0011
y	100.4	100.8	100.3	100.9	100.4

4 A product-moment correlation coefficient of 0.3275 was obtained from a sample of 40 pairs of values. Test the significance of this (a) at the 0.05 level (b) at the 0.02 level (use a two-tailed test).

5 (a) Compute the product-moment correlation coefficient for the following data giving values for S_{xx}, S_{yy} and S_{xy}.

x	2	3	4	4	5	5	6
y	7	6	5	4	3	2	1

(b) Test for these data the null hypothesis that there is no correlation between x and y. Use a 1% significance level. State any assumptions you have made.

6 (a) State the effect on the product-moment correlation coefficient between two variables x and y of

(i) changing the origin of x

(ii) changing the units of x.

(b) The following information was obtained about 8 children.

Child	A	B	C	D	E	F	G
Arithmetic mark	50	45	33	25	18	17	4
English mark	30	35	17	21	14	10	3

Calculate the product-moment correlation coefficient and use it to comment on the statement 'Those who do well at Arithmetic also do well at English'.

7 The ages X (years) and heights Y (cm) of 11 members of a football team were recorded and the following statistics were used to summarise the results.

$\sum X = 168$, $\sum Y = 1275$, $\sum XY = 20\,704$, $\sum X^2 = 2585$
$\sum Y^2 = 320\,019$

(a) Calculate the product-moment correlation coefficient for these data.

(b) Test the assertion that height and weight are positively correlated by using a suitable test. State your conclusion in words and any assumptions you have made.

8 The following data relate to the percentage of unemployment and percentage change in wages over several years.

% Unemployment (x)	1.6	2.2	2.3	1.7	1.6	2.1	2.6	1.7	1.5	1.6
% Change in wages (y)	5.0	3.2	2.7	2.1	4.1	2.7	2.9	4.6	3.5	4.4

(a) Calculate the values of S_{xx}, S_{yy}, S_{xy} and the product moment correlation coefficient between x and y.
(Use $\sum x = 18.9$; $\sum y = 35.2$; $\sum x^2 = 37.01$;
$\sum y^2 = 132.22$; $\sum xy = 64.7$.)

It has been suggested that low unemployment and a low rate of wage inflation cannot exist together.

(b) Without further calculation use your correlation coefficient to explain briefly whether or not you think the suggestion is justified. [L]

9 In a study on health a clinic investigated the age A (years), weight w (kg) and diastolic blood pressure p (mm of mercury) of a number of men, with the following results.

Age (A)	19	35	51	24	58	45	27	33	69
Weight (w)	66.7	55.2	76.2	66.7	75.0	101.6	60.3	69.9	63.9
Blood pressure (p)	55	60	80	85	75	85	70	85	85

Calculate the product-moment correlation coefficient between (a) weight and blood pressure (b) age and blood pressure.
State what can be concluded from these calculations.

10 Explain briefly your understanding of the term 'correlation'. Describe how you used, or could have used, correlation in a project or in class work.

Twelve students sat two Biology tests, one theoretical and one practical. Their marks are shown below.

Marks in theoretical test (t)	5	9	7	11	20	4	6	17	12	10	15	16
Marks in practical test (p)	6	8	9	13	20	9	8	17	14	8	17	18

(a) Draw a scatter diagram to represent these data.

(b) Find, to 3 decimal places,

(i) the value of S_{tp}

(ii) the product-moment correlation coefficient.

(c) Use a 0.05 significance level and a suitable test to check the assertion that students who do well in theoretical Biology tests also do well in practical Biology tests. [L]

11 With the help of scatter diagrams, explain the meaning of

(a) positive correlation

(b) negative correlation

(c) perfect correlation

between two variables. Describe, briefly, how you used, or could have used, correlation in a project or in class work.

In a training scheme for young people, the times they took to reach a required standard of proficiency were measured. The average training time in days for each age was recorded and the results are shown.

Age of trainees and their average training times.

Age, x(years)	16	17	18	19	20	21	22	23	24	25
Average training time, y(days)	8	6	7	9	8	11	9	10	12	11

Find the product-moment correlation coefficient between average training time and age of trainee. State whether or not your result leads you to conclude that there is a linear association between age of trainee and average training time.

[L]

3.3 Spearman's rank correlation coefficient

We have used the product-moment correlation coefficient r as a measure of the strength of association between the paired observations (x_i, y_i), $i = 1, 2 \ldots, n$, where both x and y can be measured on a continuous scale. This is reasonable when you are dealing with measurable characteristics such as height or weight, etc. There are cases where it is not possible or may not be worthwhile to measure certain variables. For example, suppose a manufacturer of tea produced a number of different blends; you could taste each blend and place the blends in order of preference. You do not, however, have a numerical scale for measuring your preference. Similarly, it may be quicker to arrange a group of individuals in order of height than to measure each one.

An ordered arrangement of n objects is called a **ranking** and the order given to an object is called its **rank**. So for n objects there will be one rank corresponding to each of the intergers 1 to n, providing that no two or more are given the same rank. When two or more are given the same rank there is said to be a **tie**. In this book we will only consider the case where there are no ties so that each object in the ranking has a unique ordinal position.

If you have two such rankings that you wish to compare, you can use the numbers given to the data to compute a correlation coefficient using the formula for the product-moment correlation coefficient. When using ranks rather than numerical data the resulting coefficient is called **Spearman's rank correlation coefficient** and is denoted by r_s.

Example 9

Two tea tasters were asked to rank nine blends of tea in their order of preference. The tea they liked best was ranked 1. Their orders of preference are shown in the table:

Blend	A	B	C	D	E	F	G	H	I
Taster 1 (x)	3	6	2	8	5	9	7	1	4
Taster 2 (y)	5	6	4	2	7	8	9	1	3

Calculate the Spearman rank correlation coefficient for these data.

x_i	y_i	x_i^2	y_i^2	x_iy_i
3	5	9	25	15
6	6	36	36	36
2	4	4	16	8
8	2	64	4	16
5	7	25	49	35
9	8	81	64	72
7	9	49	81	63
1	1	1	1	1
4	3	16	9	12
$\sum x_i = 45$	$\sum y_i = 45$	$\sum x_i^2 = 285$	$\sum y_i^2 = 285$	$\sum x_iy_i = 258$

$$r_s = \frac{S_{xy}}{\sqrt{(S_{xx}S_{yy})}} = \frac{\sum x_iy_i - \frac{\sum x_i \sum y_i}{n}}{\sqrt{\left[\left(\sum x_i^2 - \frac{(\sum x_i)^2}{n}\right)\left(\sum y_i^2 - \frac{(\sum y_i)^2}{n}\right)\right]}}$$

$$= \frac{258 - \frac{45 \times 45}{9}}{\sqrt{\left[\left(285 - \frac{45 \times 45}{9}\right)\left(285 - \frac{45 \times 45}{9}\right)\right]}}$$

$$= \frac{33}{\sqrt{(60 \times 60)}}$$

$$= 0.55$$

- **Spearman's rank correlation coefficient is derived from the product-moment correlation coefficient, so:**
  + 1 means that rankings are in perfect agreement
  – 1 means that the rankings are in exact reverse order
  0 means that there is no correlation between the rankings.

A quicker way of finding Spearman's rank correlation coefficient

If there are no ties you can speed up your calculations in the following way.

For the data $(x_i, y_i) \ldots (x_n, y_n)$ the product-moment correlation coefficient is

$$r = \frac{S_{xy}}{\sqrt{(S_{xx}S_{yy})}}$$

If x_i and y_i are ranks instead of values then

$x_1, x_2, \ldots, x_n$ are the numbers $1, 2, \ldots n$ in some order or other
$y_1, y_2, \ldots, y_n$ are the numbers $1, 2, \ldots n$ in some order or other

and

$$r_s = \frac{S_{xy}}{\sqrt{(S_{xx}S_{yy})}}$$

If there are no ties you can simplify it further by using two results.

$\sum x = \sum y = \frac{n}{2}(n+1)$ The sum of an arithmetic series

$\sum x^2 = \sum y^2 = \frac{n}{6}(n+1)(2n+1)$ The sum of the first n square numbers

(These formulae can be found in the London Examination Board's booklet of Mathematical formulae.)

So :

$$S_{xx} = S_{yy}$$

$$\Rightarrow \sum x^2{}_i - \frac{(\sum x_i)^2}{n} = \sum y^2{}_i - \frac{(\sum y_i)^2}{n}$$

$$= \tfrac{n}{6}(n+1)(2n+1) - \frac{n^2(n+1)^2}{4n}$$ (using the two formulae above)

$$= \tfrac{n}{12}(n+1)(4n+2) - \tfrac{n}{12}(n+1)(3n+3)$$ (multiplying top and bottom by 2 in the first half and by 3 in the second)

$$= \tfrac{n}{12}(n+1)(4n+2-3n-3)$$

$$= \tfrac{n}{12}(n+1)(n-1)$$

$$= \frac{n(n^2-1)}{12} \qquad (1)$$

Now

$$\sum (x_i - y_i)^2 = \sum (x_i^2 + y_i^2 - 2x_iy_i)$$ (multiplying out)

$$= \sum x_i^2 + \sum y_i^2 - \sum 2x_iy_i$$ (removing the bracket)

so

$$\frac{\sum 2x_iy_i}{2} = \frac{\sum x_i^2 + \sum y_i^2 - \sum (x_i - y_i)^2}{2}$$ (rearranging the formula and dividing by 2)

$$\sum x_iy_i = \frac{\sum x_i^2 + \sum y_i^2}{2} - \frac{\sum (x_i - y_i)^2}{2}$$

But

$$\sum x_i^2 = \sum y_i^2 = \tfrac{n}{6}(n+1)(2n+1)$$

So:

$$\sum x_iy_i = \tfrac{n}{6}(n+1)(2n+1) - \tfrac{1}{2}\sum (x_i - y_i)^2$$

Thus $$S_{xy} = \sum x_i y_i - \frac{\sum x_i \sum y_i}{n}$$

$$= \tfrac{n}{6}(n+1)(2n+1) - \tfrac{1}{2}\sum(x_i - y_i)^2 - \frac{n^2(n+1)^2}{4n}$$

$$= \frac{n(n^2-1)}{12} - \tfrac{1}{2}\sum(x_i - y_i)^2 \qquad (2)$$

Substituting equations (1) and (2) in the formula $r_s = \dfrac{S_{xy}}{\sqrt{(S_{xx}S_{yy})}}$ gives:

$$r_s = \frac{\dfrac{n(n^2-1)}{12} - \tfrac{1}{2}\sum(x_i - y_i)^2}{\sqrt{\left(\dfrac{n(n^2-1)}{12} \times \dfrac{n(n^2-1)}{12}\right)}}$$

$$= \frac{\tfrac{n}{12}(n^2-1) - \tfrac{1}{2}\sum(x_i - y_i)^2}{\dfrac{n(n^2-1)}{12}}$$

$$= 1 - \frac{6\sum(x_i - y_i)^2}{n(n^2-1)}$$

We usually denote $(x_i - y_i)$ by the letter d and write:

■ $\boldsymbol{r_s = 1 - \dfrac{6\sum d^2}{n(n^2-1)}}$

The above proof depends upon there being no ties and the formula may only be used if this condition is met. You will not be expected to know this proof.

The formula

$$r_s = 1 - \frac{6\sum d^2}{n(n^2-1)}$$

reduces the amount of work you need to do to find r_s if you do not have a statistical calculator. If you have a calculator, the ranks may be input in the same way as for r, but you must remember the figure given is r_s and not r.

Example 10

During a cattle show two judges ranked the ten cattle for quality according to the following table.

Cattle	A	B	C	D	E	F	G	H	I	J
Judge A	1	5	2	6	4	8	3	7	10	9
Judge B	3	6	2	7	5	8	1	4	9	10

Find Spearman's rank correlation coefficient between the two judges and comment on the result.

A	B	d	d^2
1	3	−2	4
5	6	−1	1
2	2	0	0
6	7	−1	1
4	5	−1	1
8	8	0	0
3	1	2	4
7	4	3	9
10	9	1	1
9	10	−1	1
			$\sum d^2 = 22$

$$r_s = 1 - \frac{6 \times 22}{10(100 - 1)} = 0.867$$

There is a reasonable degree of agreement between the two judges. In an examination you do not need to show the table, but you should show the value of $\sum d^2$.

Example 11

The marks of eight pupils in French and German language tests were as follows.

Student	A	B	C	D	E	F	G	H
French, f (%)	52	25	86	33	55	57	54	46
German, g (%)	40	48	65	57	41	39	63	34

Calculate

(a) the product-moment correlation coefficient for f and g
(b) Spearman's rank correlation coefficient for f and g

and plot the scatter diagram for each.

(a)

	f	g	f^2	g^2	fg
	52	40	2704	1600	2080
	25	48	625	2304	1200
	86	65	7396	4225	5590
	33	57	1089	3249	1881
	55	41	3025	1681	2255
	57	39	3249	1521	2223
	54	63	2916	3969	3402
	46	34	2116	1156	1564
Totals	**408**	**387**	**23 120**	**19 705**	**20 195**

$$r = \frac{S_{fg}}{\sqrt{(S_{ff}S_{gg})}} = \frac{\sum fg - \frac{\sum f \sum g}{n}}{\sqrt{\left[\left(\sum f^2 - \frac{(\sum f)^2}{n}\right)\left(\sum g^2 - \frac{(\sum g)^2}{n}\right)\right]}}$$

$$= \frac{20\,195 - \frac{408 \times 387}{8}}{\sqrt{\left[\left(23\,120 - \frac{408^2}{8}\right)\left(19\,705 - \frac{387^2}{8}\right)\right]}}$$

$$= 0.304$$

(b)

f	g	rank f	rank g	d	d^2
52	40	5	6	−1	1
25	48	8	4	4	16
86	65	1	1	0	0
33	57	7	3	4	16
55	41	3	5	−2	4
57	39	2	7	−5	25
54	63	4	2	2	4
46	34	6	8	−2	4
					$\sum d^2 = 70$

$$\begin{aligned} r_s &= 1 - \frac{6\sum d^2}{n(n^2 - 1)} \\ &= 1 - \frac{6 \times 70}{8(64 - 1)} \\ &= 0.1666\ldots \end{aligned}$$

The scatter diagrams look like this:

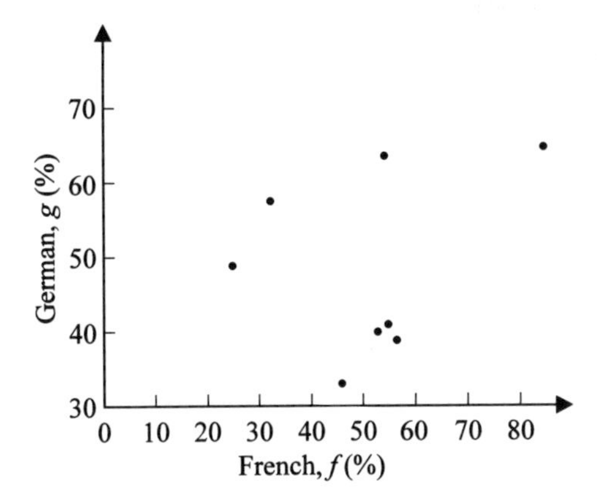

Scatter diagram for f and g

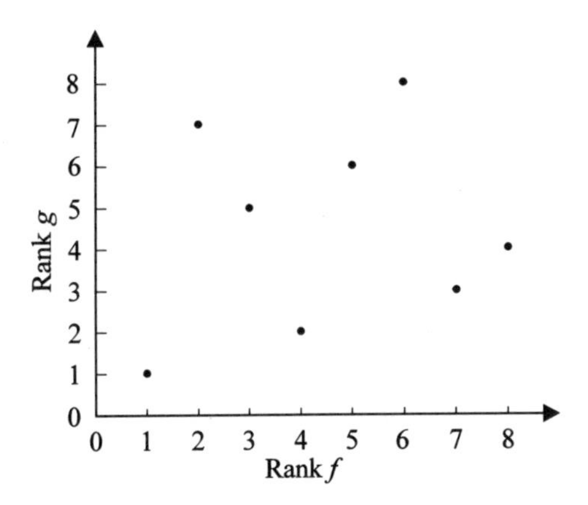

Scatter diagram for rank f and rank g

You can see from the results of example 11 that the values of r and r_s are not the same when you use the same data. Because of the loss of detail in ranking, the value of r is in general more accurate as a measure of correlation than r_s. The product-moment correlation coefficient and Spearman's rank correlation coefficient measure different things. You can see that the scatter diagrams for example 11 do not look the same. The difference may be seen even more in the following data, for which $r = 0.895$ and $r_s = 1$:

x	10	20	30	40
y	23	35	39	89
Rank x	1	2	3	4
Rank y	1	2	3	4

The scatter diagrams for x and y, and rank x and rank y are shown below.

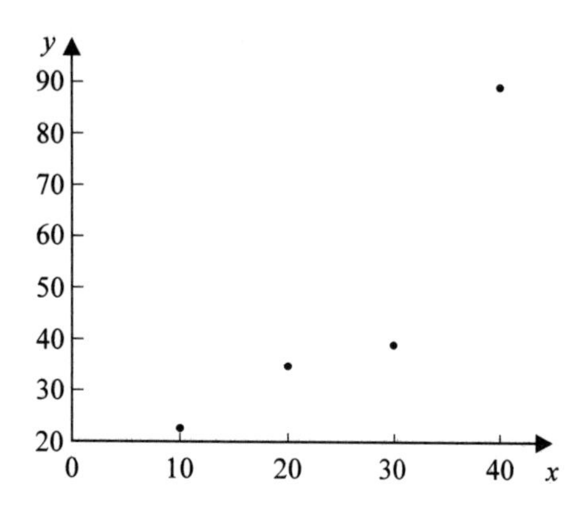

Scatter diagram for x and y

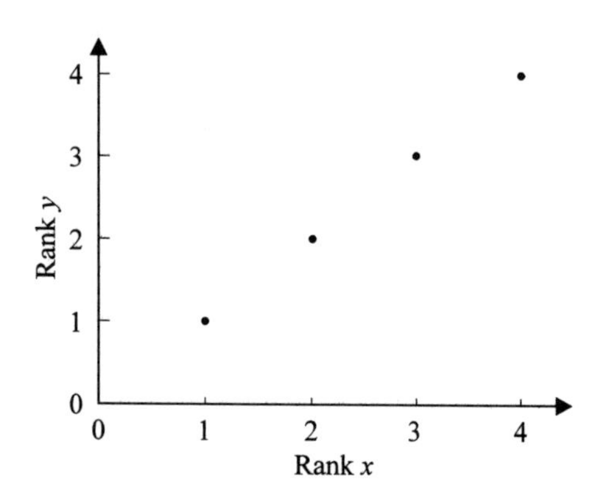

Scatter diagram for rank x and rank y

You might wonder what happens to Spearman's rank correlation coefficient when the product-moment correlation coefficient is negative. Consider the following data with $r = -0.9152$ and $r_s = -0.8$.

x	10	20	30	40
y	82	40	46	12
Rank x	1	2	3	4
Rank y	4	2	3	1

The scatter diagrams for these data are shown below:

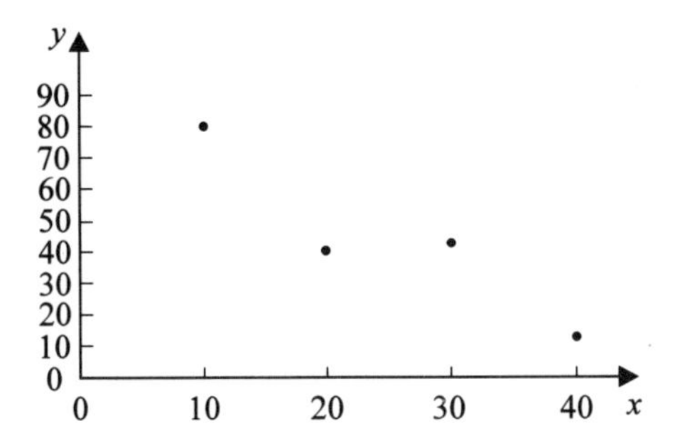

Scatter diagram for x and y

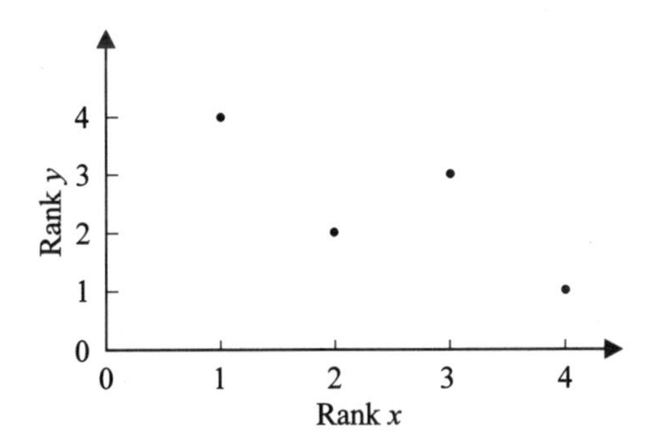

Scatter diagram for rank x and rank y

In order to test if the product-moment correlation coefficient of the population (ρ) is zero you must assume that there is a joint normal distribution between the values of X and Y.

Spearman's rank correlation does not assume this and may be used when the variables do not fulfil these conditions, and where a test of this sort is required. Spearman's rank correlation coefficient is also generally more suitable where X and Y are discrete variables, or where they cannot be measured but may be placed in order of preference.

Testing the hypothesis that Spearman's population rank correlation coefficient is zero

Since Spearman's rank correlation coefficient was derived from the product-moment correlation coefficient, you might expect r_s to have a similar distribution when $\rho = 0$. Table 6 on page 209 gives minimum values for r_s at the 0.05, 0.025 and 0.01 (5%, 2.5% and 1%) levels for different values of n from 4 upwards.

For a sample size of 10 you see from the table that the minimum value of r_s to be significant at the 0.05 level on a one-tailed test is 0.5636.

As before, you start with a null hypothesis H_0: $\rho = 0$ and use as your alternative hypothesis H_1: $\rho \neq 0$ (two-tailed test) or H_1: $\rho > 0$ or H_1: $\rho < 0$ (one-tailed test).

Example 12

A rank correlation coefficient was found to be $r_s = 0.773$ from a ranking of $n = 6$. Is this significantly different from 0 at the 5% level?

H_0: $\rho = 0$ The correlation is zero.
H_1: $\rho \neq 0$ The correlation is either positive or it is negative.

From the tables for a sample size of 6 at the 0.05 significance level the critical values are ± 0.8857.

But $r = 0.773$, so the result is not significant at the 0.05 level. You do not reject H_0. There is no evidence to suggest that $\rho \neq 0$.

Example 13

The popularity of 16 subjects at a comprehensive school was found by counting the number of boys and the number of girls who chose each subject and then ranking the subjects. The results are shown in the table below.

Subject	A	B	C	D	E	F	G	H	I	J	K	L	M	N	O	P
Boys' ranks, b	2	5	9	8	1	3	15	16	6	10	12	14	4	7	11	13
Girls' ranks, g	4	7	11	3	6	9	12	16	5	13	10	8	2	1	15	14

Calculate Spearman's rank correlation coefficient and use a suitable test at the 1% level to investigate the statement, 'boys' and girls' choices are positively correlated'.

Using a calculator: $\sum d^2 = 214$

$$r_s = 1 - \frac{6\sum d^2}{n(n^2 - 1)}$$

$$= 1 - \frac{6 \times 214}{16(16^2 - 1)}$$

$$= 0.685$$

H_0: $\rho = 0$ (There is no correlation.)
H_1: $\rho > 0$ (The choices are positively correlated.)

From the tables for a sample size of 16 the critical value is 0.5824. Since 0.685 > 0.5824, the result is significant at the 1% level.

You reject H_0: boys' and girls' choices *are* positively correlated.

Exercise 3B

(Use a 5% significance level unless stated otherwise.)

1 For each of the data sets of ranks given below, calculate the Spearman's rank correlation coefficient and interpret the result.

(a)

x	1	2	3	4	5	6
y	3	2	1	5	4	6

(b)

x	1	2	3	4	5	6	7	8	9	10
y	2	1	4	3	5	8	7	9	6	10

(c)

x	5	2	6	1	4	3	7	8
y	5	6	3	8	7	4	2	1

2 The number of goals scored by football teams and their positions in the league were recorded as follows for the top 12 teams.

Team	A	B	C	D	E	F	G	H	I	J	K	L
Goals	49	44	43	36	40	39	29	21	28	30	33	26
League position	1	2	3	4	5	6	7	8	9	10	11	12

(a) Find $\sum d^2$.

(b) Calculate Spearman's rank correlation coefficient for these data. What conclusions can be drawn from this result?

3 A sample of a class's statistics projects was taken, and the projects were assessed by two teachers independently. Each teacher decided their rank order with the following results.

Project	A	B	C	D	E	F	G	H
Teacher A	5	8	1	6	2	7	3	4
Teacher B	7	4	3	1	6	8	2	5

(a) Find $\sum d^2$.

(b) Calculate the rank correlation coefficient and state any conclusions you draw from it.

4 A veterinary surgeon and a trainee veterinary surgeon both rank a small herd of cows for quality. Their rankings are shown below.

Cow	A	D	F	E	B	C	H	J
Qualified vet	1	2	3	4	5	6	7	8
Trainee vet	1	2	5	6	4	3	8	7

Find the rank correlation coefficient for these data, and comment on the experience of the trainee vet.

5 Two adjudicators at an ice dance skating competition award marks as follows.

Competition	A	B	C	D	E	F	G	H	I	J
Judge 1	7.8	6.6	7.3	7.4	8.4	6.5	8.9	8.5	6.7	7.7
Judge 2	8.1	6.8	8.2	7.5	8	6.7	8.5	8.3	6.6	7.8

(a) Explain why you would use Spearman's rank correlation coefficient in this case.

(b) Calculate the rank correlation coefficient r_s, and comment on how well the judges agree.

6 (a) A teacher believes that he can predict the positions in which his students will finish in an A-level examination. When the results were out he wished to compare his predictions with the actual results. What correlation test should he use and why?

(b) The table shows predicted and actual orders.

Student	A	B	C	D	E	F	G	H	I	J
Predicted, p	2	4	1	3	8	6	9	5	10	7
Actual, a	3	4	2	8	1	6	7	9	10	5

Calculate Spearman's rank correlation coefficient r_s between a and p. Comment on the result.

7 A doctor assessed the lung damage suffered by a number of his patients who smoked, and asked each one 'For how many years have you smoked?', with the following results.

Patient	A	B	C	D	E	F	G
No. of years smoked	15	22	25	28	30	31	42
Lung damage grade	30	50	55	35	40	42	58

Calculate Spearman's rank correlation coefficient r_s and comment on the result. Give your value of $\sum d^2$.

8 Each of the teams in a school hockey league had the total number of goals scored by them and against them recorded, with the following results.

Team	A	B	C	D	E	F	G
Goals for	39	40	28	27	26	30	42
Goals against	22	28	27	42	24	38	23

Investigate whether there is any correlation between the goals for and those against by using Spearman's rank correlation coefficient. Use a suitable test at the 1% level to investigate the statement, 'A team that scores a lot of goals concedes very few goals'.

9 A Spearman's rank correlation obtained from the fuel consumption of a selection of 30 cars and their engine sizes gave a rank correlation coefficient $r_s = 0.5321$. Investigate whether or not the fuel consumption is related to the engine size. State your null and alternative hypotheses. (Use a 5% level of significance.)

10 The weekly takings and weekly profits for six branch shops of a firm are set out below.

Shop	1	2	3	4	5	6
Takings (£)	4000	6200	3600	5100	5000	3800
Profits (£)	400	1100	450	750	800	500

(a) Calculate the coefficient of rank correlation r_s between the takings and profit.

(b) It is assumed that profits and takings will be positively correlated. Using a suitable hypothesis test (stating the null and alternative hypotheses) test this assertion at the 5% level of significance.

11 The rankings of 12 students in Mathematics and Music were as follows.

Maths	1	2	3	4	5	6	7	8	9	10	11	12
Music	6	4	2	3	1	7	5	9	10	8	11	12

(a) Calculate the coefficient of rank correlation r_S. [Show your value of $\sum d^2$.]

(b) Test the assertion that there is no correlation between these subjects. State the null and alternative hypotheses used.

12 (a) A child is asked to place 10 objects in order and gives the ordering

A C H F B D G E J I

The correct ordering is

A B C D E F G H I J

Find a coefficient of rank correlation between the child's ordering and the correct ordering.

(b) Use a 5% significance level and a suitable test to draw conclusions about this result. [L]

13 The crop of a root vegetable was measured over six consecutive years which were ranked for wetness. The results are given in the table below.

Year	1	2	3	4	5	6
Crop (10 000 tons)	62	73	52	77	63	61
Rank of wetness	5	4	1	6	3	2

Calculate, to 3 decimal places, a Spearman's rank correlation coefficient for these data. Test the assertion that crop and wetness are not correlated. [L]

SUMMARY OF KEY POINTS

1 $S_{xy} = \sum(x_i - \bar{x})(y_i - \bar{y}) = \sum x_i y_i - \frac{\sum x_i \sum y_i}{n}$

$S_{xx} = \sum(x_i - \bar{x})^2 = \sum x_i^2 - \frac{(\sum x_i)^2}{n}$

$S_{yy} = \sum(y_i - \bar{y})^2 = \sum y_i^2 - \frac{(\sum y_i)^2}{n}$

2 Product-moment correlation coefficient is

$$r = \frac{S_{xy}}{\sqrt{(S_{xx}S_{yy})}}$$

r is not affected by changes in scale or change of origin.

3 Spearman's rank correlation coefficient is

$$r_s = 1 - \frac{6\sum d^2}{n(n^2 - 1)} \text{ where } d_i = (x_i - y_i)$$

Regression

4

4.1 Independent and dependent variables

In the physical sciences we often set up investigations or experiments in which we try to find a relationship between two variables. For example, in your science work you may have done an experiment to investigate the relationship between the mass x hung on a spring and its length y. The purpose of such investigations is to find a law connecting the variables x and y that allows you to predict the value of y for any given value of x.

In the spring experiment you can choose the values to set for the mass x and observe the resulting values of the length y. If there is a relationship between the variables then the y values are said to depend on the x values. For this reason y is called the **dependent variable**. The values of x are only dependent on the experimenter's choice so x is called the **independent variable**. (Sometimes the independent variable is called the explanatory variable and the dependent variable is called the response variable.)

We usually assume that we can set the values of the independent variable accurately but that our observations of the values of the dependent variable will be subject to some level of error or natural variation.

4.2 Scatter diagrams

One way of seeing if there is a relationship between the independent and dependent variables is to plot the points (x_i, y_i), for $i = 1$ to n, on a scatter diagram. When drawing a scatter diagram, the independent variable is always plotted horizontally and the dependent variable is plotted vertically.

Here are some results from an experiment in which different masses were placed on a spring and the resulting length measured:

Mass, x (kg)	20	40	60	80	100
Length, y (cm)	48	55.1	56.3	61.2	68

When plotted on a scatter diagram these data look like this:

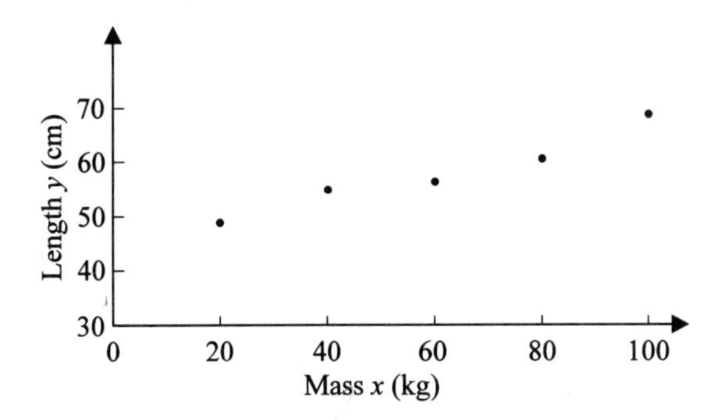

From the scatter diagram it looks as though a straight line could represent the relationship between the variables. (You may recall from your science work that there is a straight-line relationship known as Hooke's Law.) But in the diagram you can see that not all the points will fit onto a straight line. This is because of the errors in y.

By looking at scatter diagrams you may be able to see if a straight line would be a good model for the relationship between x and y or whether a curve is more appropriate. Here are three possible models:

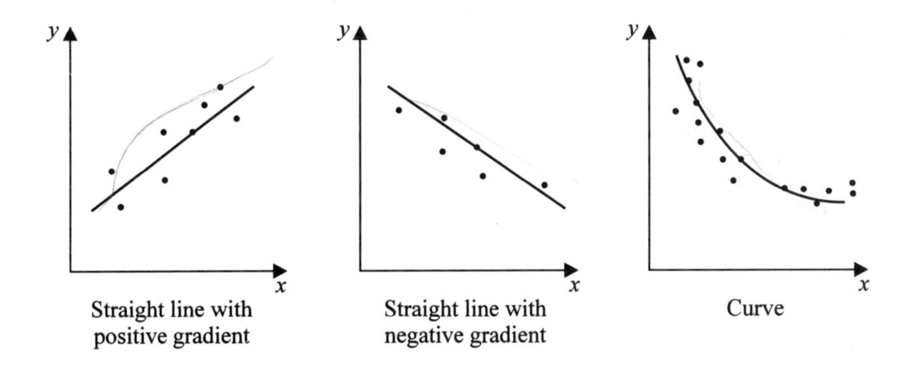

If you drew a straight line through the points of the right-hand scatter diagram the points would lie above the line at either end and below the line in the middle. This pattern is an indication that a curve is a better model.

In this chapter we will consider only relationships in which a straight line is the appropriate model. This is called a **linear relationship**. We start by looking at the straight-line law.

4.3 The straight-line law $y = \alpha + \beta x$

All straight-line laws are defined by an equation of the form $y = \alpha + \beta x$ where α and β are constants; for example, if α is 5 and β is 3 then $y = 5 + 3x$ is a straight line.

For the equation $y = \alpha + \beta x$, when $x = 0$, $y = \alpha$. Also when $x = 1$, $y = \alpha + \beta$. The graph of the equation looks like this:

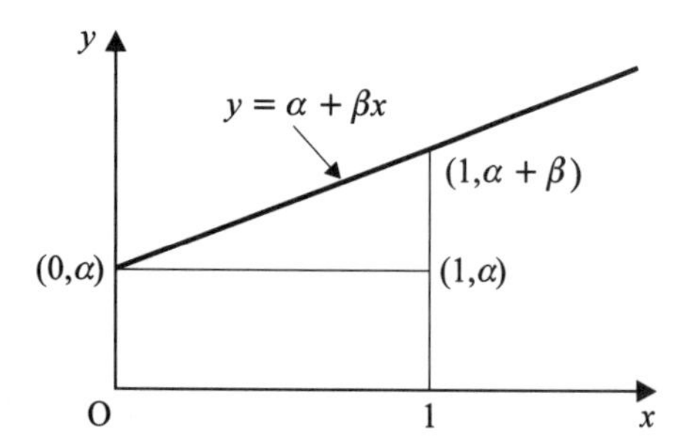

In the diagram you can see that $(0, \alpha)$ is the point at which the line cuts the y-axis. We call this the ***y*-intercept**. As the coordinates of the point where $x = 1$ are $(1, \alpha + \beta)$, the gradient of the line is

$$\text{gradient} = \frac{\text{change in } y}{\text{change in } x} = \frac{(\alpha + \beta) - \alpha}{1 - 0} = \beta$$

So β is the **gradient** of the line. To look at it in a different way, β is the amount by which the dependent variable increases for an increase of 1 in the independent variable.

If β is positive, y increases as x increases and the gradient is said to be positive. If β is negative, y decreases as x increases and the gradient is said to be negative.

The linear regression model

When the results of an investigation are modelled by the straight-line law $y = \alpha + \beta x$, each of the values y_i will have an associated experimental error ε_i which may be positive or negative. Each y_i is expressed in terms of x_i as

$$y_i = \alpha + \beta x_i + \varepsilon_i$$

Errors usually occur due to natural variations and are equally disposed about a mean value of zero. The probability distribution that is taken by these errors is a normal distribution. This is written as $\varepsilon_i = \mathrm{N}(0, \sigma^2)$.

- **The linear regression model:**

$$\boldsymbol{y_i = \alpha + \beta x_i + \varepsilon_i}, \quad \textbf{where } \boldsymbol{\varepsilon_i \sim \mathrm{N}(0, \sigma^2)}$$

Having assumed the linear regression model, you must use the experimental results to find the law. When the law is plotted the resulting line is called a **regression line**.

If you assume a linear regression, each point with coordinates (x_i, y_i) will be a vertical distance ε_i from the regression line as shown:

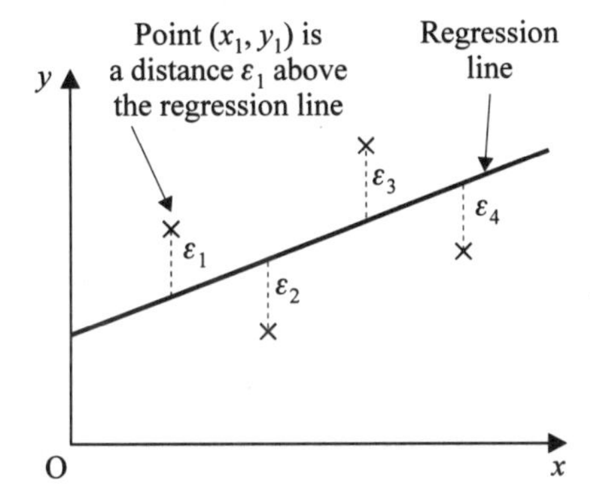

You do not know the magnitude of the errors (ε_i) in your measurements. If the errors are very small a line may be drawn through the points by eye, and this is sometimes done. If the errors are normally distributed it can be shown that the **line of best fit** (the one that gives unbiased estimates for α and β) is the one found by the method of least squares. The method of least squares was formulated by the French mathematician Legendre, and the resulting line is known as the **least squares regression line**.

4.4 The least squares regression line

The least squares regression line is drawn between the points representing the observations in such a way that the sum of the squares of the vertical distances between the line and the points plotted $(\sum \varepsilon_i^2)$ is minimised.

The assumed linear regression model is: $y_i = \alpha + \beta x_i + \varepsilon_i$, where $\varepsilon_i \sim \mathrm{N}(0, \sigma^2)$, the underlying law relating x and y being $y = \alpha + \beta x$.

If you use the best estimates $\bar{x}$ and $\bar{y}$ for the means of x and y you can write:

$$\bar{y} = \alpha + \beta\bar{x}$$

or

$$\alpha = \bar{y} - \beta\bar{x}$$

Now, using your sample values:

$$\begin{aligned}
y_i &= \alpha + \beta x_i + \varepsilon_i \\
\varepsilon_i &= y_i - \alpha - \beta x_i \\
\varepsilon_i^2 &= (y_i - \alpha - \beta x_i)^2 \\
\sum \varepsilon_i^2 &= \sum (y_i - \alpha - \beta x_i)^2 \\
&= \sum (y_i - \bar{y} + \beta\bar{x} - \beta x_i)^2 && \text{(substituting for } \alpha\text{)} \\
&= \sum [(y_i - \bar{y}) - \beta(x_i - \bar{x})]^2 \\
&= \sum [(y_i - \bar{y})^2 - 2\beta(x_i - \bar{x})(y_i - \bar{y}) + \beta^2(x_i - \bar{x})^2] && \text{(multiplying out)} \\
&= \sum (y_i - \bar{y})^2 - 2\beta \sum (x_i - \bar{x})(y_i - \bar{y}) + \beta^2 \sum (x_i - \bar{x})^2
\end{aligned}$$

Except for β, the expressions above are all just numbers, so you can differentiate with respect to β:

$$\frac{\mathrm{d}(\sum \varepsilon_i^2)}{\mathrm{d}\beta} = -2\sum (x_i - \bar{x})(y_i - \bar{y}) + 2\beta \sum (x_i - \bar{x})^2$$

To make $\sum \varepsilon_i^2$ a minimum, let $\frac{\mathrm{d}\sum \varepsilon_i^2}{\mathrm{d}\beta} = 0$. This fixes a value for β and a value for α (since $\alpha = \bar{y} - \beta\bar{x}$). The values of α and β will be different for each sample. We write $\hat{\alpha}$ and $\hat{\beta}$ (pronounced α hat and β hat) instead of α and β to show that we are estimating. As has already been said, these values $\hat{\alpha}$ and $\hat{\beta}$ obtained using the methods of least squares will be unbiased estimates for α and β.

If $\frac{\mathrm{d}\sum \varepsilon_i^2}{\mathrm{d}\beta} = 0$, then

$$0 = -2\sum (x_i - \bar{x})(y_i - \bar{y}) + 2\hat{\beta} \sum (x_i - \bar{x})^2$$

and

$$\hat{\beta} = \frac{\sum (x_i - \bar{x})(y_i - \bar{y})}{\sum (x_i - \bar{x})^2}$$

In chapter 3 we denoted: $\sum (x_i - \bar{x})(y_i - \bar{y})$ as S_{xy} and $\sum (x_i - \bar{x})^2$ as S_{xx}.

So:

■

$$\hat{\beta} = \frac{S_{xy}}{S_{xx}}$$

$\hat{\alpha}$ may be found by:

$$y_i = \hat{\alpha} + \hat{\beta}x_i$$

$$\sum y_i = n\hat{\alpha} + \hat{\beta}\sum x_i$$

$$\frac{\sum y_i}{n} = \hat{\alpha} + \hat{\beta}\frac{\sum x_i}{n} \qquad \text{(dividing by } n\text{)}$$

$$\hat{\alpha} = \frac{\sum y_i}{n} - \hat{\beta}\frac{\sum x_i}{n} \qquad \text{(by transposition)}$$

■ $$\hat{\alpha} = \bar{y} - \hat{\beta}\bar{x}$$

(since $\bar{y} = \frac{\sum y_i}{n}$ and $\bar{x} = \frac{\sum x_i}{n}$)

(You will not be asked to prove these equations.)

■ **The equation of the regression line of y on x is:**

$$y = \hat{\alpha} + \hat{\beta}x$$

where $$\hat{\beta} = \frac{S_{xy}}{S_{xx}} \text{ and } \hat{\alpha} = \bar{y} - \hat{\beta}\bar{x}$$

Example 1

(a) Explain, very briefly, the method of least squares for obtaining the equation of a regression line.

(b) The number of grams g of a certain detergent which will dissolve in 100 g of water at temperature t°C is shown in the table.

t (°C)	0	10	20	30	40	50	60	70	80	90	100
g (g)	53.5	59.5	65.2	70.6	75.5	80.2	85.5	90.0	95.0	99.2	104.0

Obtain the equation of the least squares regression line of g on t. Estimate the value of g for a temperature of 45°C. [L]

(a)

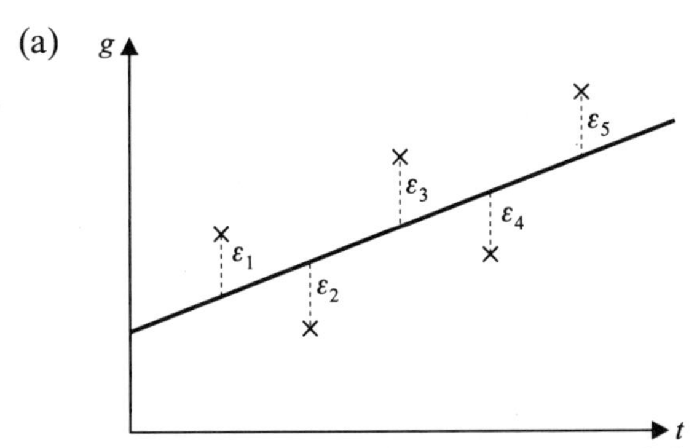

The lengths shown are the errors ε_i, $i = 1, 2, \ldots, n$.
In the least squares method the $\sum \varepsilon_i^2$ is minimised.

(b)

t_i	g_i	t_ig_i	t_i^2
0	53.5	0	0
10	59.5	595	100
20	65.2	1304	400
30	70.6	2118	900
40	75.5	3020	1600
50	80.2	4010	2500
60	85.5	5130	3600
70	90.0	6300	4900
80	95.0	7600	6400
90	99.2	8928	8100
100	104.0	10 400	10 000
$\sum t_i = 550$	$\sum g_i = 878.2$	$\sum t_ig_i = 49\,405$	$\sum t_i^2 = 38\,500$

$$S_{tg} = \sum t_ig_i - \frac{\sum t_i \sum g_i}{n} = 49\,405 - \frac{550 \times 878.2}{11} = 5495$$

$$S_{tt} = \sum t_i^2 - \frac{(\sum t_i)^2}{n} = 38\,500 - \frac{550 \times 550}{11} = 11\,000$$

$$\hat{\beta} = \frac{S_{tg}}{S_{tt}} = \frac{5495}{11\,000}$$
$$= 0.4995 \text{ (4 d.p.)}$$

$$\hat{\alpha} = \bar{g} - \hat{\beta}\bar{t}$$
$$= \frac{878.2}{11} - \frac{0.4995 \times 550}{11}$$
$$= 54.86 \text{ (2 d.p.)}$$

The regression line is $g = 54.86 + 0.4995t$

If $t = 45$ $\quad g = 54.86 + 0.4995 \times 45$
$$= 77.34\ ^\circ\text{C (2 d.p.)}$$

In the example the calculation has been laid out in a tabular form so that you can see what is going on. You may instead calculate the required values of $\hat{\alpha}$ and $\hat{\beta}$ by using a calculator. It is suggested that if you use a calculator then you should show sufficient working and not simply write down the answer. If you get the answer wrong you will then be given credit for any correct work done. Example 1 might appear as:

$$\sum t_i = 550 \qquad \sum g_i = 878.2$$

$$\bar{t} = 50 \qquad \bar{g} = 79.836$$

$$\sum t_i g_i = 49\,405 \qquad \sum t_i^2 = 38\,500$$

$$S_{tg} = 49\,405 - \frac{550 \times 878.2}{11} = 5495$$

$$S_{tt} = 38\,500 - \frac{550 \times 550}{11} = 11\,000$$

$$\hat{\beta} = \frac{S_{tg}}{S_{tt}} = \frac{5495}{11\,000}$$
$$= 0.4995$$

$$\hat{\alpha} = \bar{g} - \hat{\beta}\bar{t}$$
$$= 79.836 - \frac{0.4995 \times 550}{11}$$
$$= 54.86$$

If $t = 45$

$$g = 54.86 + 0.4995 \times 45$$
$$= 77.34\ ^\circ\text{C}$$

4.5 Using regression lines

Now that you have a model for your results in the form of a regression line, it is possible to use the equation of the regression line to make estimates of the mean value of the dependent variable for any given value of the independent variable within the range of the data. This process is called **interpolation**. You must remember, however, that you do not know what happens *outside* the range of your experimental values. In the case of the spring experiment mentioned earlier, there is a mass which, when applied to the spring, causes it to break, and long before this load is reached the linear relationship fails to hold. When values outside the range of the experimental results are found the process is called **extrapolation**. You should not, in general, extrapolate and you must view any extrapolated values with caution.

When looking at the straight-line law earlier in the chapter you will have seen that α is the intercept of the line on the y-axis (the value of

y when $x = 0$) and β is the gradient of the line (the amount by which y increases for an increase of 1 in x, sometimes called the rate of change of y with respect to x). These may have some meaning within the context of the investigation you are making, and you should be prepared to interpret them, as is done in the next example.

Example 2

A scientist working in agricultural research believes that there is a linear relationship between the amount of a certain food supplement given to hens and the hardness of the shells of the eggs they lay. As an experiment, controlled quantities of the supplement were added to the hens' normal diet and the hardness of the shells of the eggs was then measured on a scale from 1 to 10, with the following results:

Food supplement, f(g/day)	2	4	6	8	10	12	14
Hardness of shells, g	3.2	5.2	5.5	6.4	7.2	8.5	9.8

(a) Find the equation of the regression line.
(b) Explain what the values of $\hat{\alpha}$ and $\hat{\beta}$ tell you and why you should not try to calculate the shell hardness for a food supplement of 20 g per day.

(a)
$$\sum f_i = 56 \qquad \sum g_i = 45.8$$
$$\bar{f} = 8 \qquad \bar{g} = 6.543$$
$$\sum f_i^2 = 560 \qquad \sum f_i g_i = 422.6$$

$$S_{fg} = 422.6 - \frac{56 \times 45.8}{7} = 56.2$$
$$S_{ff} = 560 - \frac{(56)^2}{7} = 112$$

$$\hat{\beta} = \frac{S_{fg}}{S_{ff}} = \frac{56.2}{112}$$
$$= 0.5018 \text{ hardness units per g per day}$$

$$\hat{\alpha} = \bar{g} - \hat{\beta}\bar{f}$$
$$= 6.543 - 0.5018 \times 8$$
$$= 2.5286 \text{ hardness units}$$

$$g = 2.5286 + 0.5018f$$

(b) $\hat{\alpha}$ tells you the eggshell strength when no supplement is given (i.e. when $f = 0$). Zero is only just outside the range of f so it is quite reasonable to use this value. $\hat{\beta}$ tells you the rate at which the hardness increases with increased food supplement, in this case for every extra 1 g of food supplement per day the hardness increases by 0.5018 hardness units. The value of 20 g for f is well outside the range of f and would be very unreliable.

Exercise 4A

1 Find the regression line of y on x for the following data:

x	2	4	5	8	10
y	3	7	8	13	17

2 The relationship between the number of coats of paint applied to a yacht and the resulting weather resistance was tested in a laboratory. One year's weathering on the yacht was simulated by one month's corrosion in the laboratory. The table shows the results of this experiment, when one month's corrosion is changed to 1 year's weathering on the yacht.

Coats of paint (x)	1	2	3	4	5
Protection (years) (y)	1.4	2.9	4.1	5.8	7.2

Find the equation of a suitable regression line for protection on coats of paint.

3 For the following data

(a) find the mean values $\bar{x}$ and $\bar{y}$, and using these find the equation of the regression line for y on x in the form $(y_i - \bar{y}) = \beta(x_i - \bar{x})$.

(b) Plot a scatter diagram and draw the regression line of y on x.

x	6	8	10	12	14
y	102	106	110	113	120

4 (a) By plotting a scatter diagram for the following data suggest a possible relationship between x and y.

(b) Calculate the least squares regression line for these data. Give values for S_{xy} and S_{xx}.

x	10	20	30	40	50	60	70
y	16	14.8	14.6	11.6	13.1	11.0	9.7

5 The variables H and T are known to be linearly related. Fifty pairs of experimental observations of the two variables gave the following results:

$$\sum H = 83.4 \qquad \sum T = 402.0 \qquad \sum HT = 680.2$$
$$\sum H^2 = 384.6 \qquad \sum T^2 = 3238.2$$

Obtain the regression equation from which one can estimate H when T has the value 7.8, and give, to 1 decimal place, the value of this estimate. [L]

6 The accountant of a company monitors the number of items produced per month by the company, together with the total cost of production. The following table shows the data collected for a random sample of 12 months.

Number of items (x) (1000s)	21	39	48	24	72	75	15	35	62	81	12	56
Production cost (y) (£1000)	40	58	67	45	89	96	37	53	83	102	35	75

(a) Plot these data on a scatter diagram. Explain why this diagram would support the fitting of a regression equation of y on x.

(b) Find an equation for the regression line of y on x in the form $y = \alpha + \beta x$.

(Use $\sum x^2 = 30\,786$; $\sum xy = 41\,444$.)

The selling price of each item produced is £2.20.

(c) Find the level of output at which total income and total costs are equal. Interpret this value. [L]

7 A drilling machine can run at various speeds, but in general the higher the speed the sooner the drill needs to be replaced. Over several months, 15 pairs of observations relating to speed, s revolutions per minute, and life of drill, h hours, are collected. For convenience the data are coded so that $x = s - 20$ and $y = h - 100$ and the following summations obtained:

$$\sum x = 143;\ \sum y = 391;\ \sum x^2 = 2413;\ \sum y^2 = 22\,441;\ \sum xy = 484$$

(a) Find the equation of the regression line of h on s.

(b) Interpret the slope of your regression line.

(c) Estimate the life of a drill revolving at 30 revolutions per minute. [L]

8 The table below shows the age A and the strontium ratio S for each of 10 basalt rock samples, one sample of each age being specifically chosen for the exercise.

Ages and strontium ratios of rock samples

A (10^2 Ma)	1	2	3	4	5
S	0.710	0.723	0.738	0.751	0.765

A (10^2 Ma)	6	7	8	9	10
S	0.780	0.793	0.808	0.824	0.840

Find the values of $\bar{A}$ and $\bar{S}$.

Given that $\sum AS = 43.710$, obtain the equation of the regression line of strontium ratio on age.

Estimate the strontium ratio for a basalt rock sample of age 3.5×10^2 Ma. [L]

9 Distinguish between the independent and the dependent variables in a linear regression.

In an experiment, the atomic heat, H units, of an element was measured at various temperatures, T degrees absolute (degrees Kelvin). The results are shown in the table:

T	100	150	200	250	300	350	400	450	500
H	0	0.38	0.8	1.22	1.6	2	2.42	2.8	3.18

Draw a scatter diagram to exhibit the data. Mark the means of T and H on your diagram.

Given that $\sum TH = 5520$, obtain the equation of the regression line of atomic heat on absolute temperature.
From your equation, estimate the increase in the atomic heat of the element when its temperature is increased by 100 degrees absolute. [L]

10 A chemist measured the speed, y, of an enzymatic reaction at 12 different concentrations, x, of the substrate and the results are given below.

x	$\frac{1}{2}$	$\frac{1}{3}$	$\frac{1}{4}$	$\frac{1}{5}$	$\frac{1}{6}$	$\frac{1}{7}$
y	0.204	0.218	0.189	0.269	0.172	0.142

x	$\frac{1}{8}$	$\frac{1}{9}$	$\frac{1}{10}$	$\frac{1}{11}$	$\frac{1}{12}$	$\frac{1}{13}$
y	0.149	0.111	0.125	0.123	0.112	0.096

The chemist thought that the model relating y and x could be of the form

$$y = a + \frac{b}{x}$$

(a) Plot a scatter diagram of y against $\frac{1}{x}$.

(b) Ignoring the observation $(\frac{1}{5}, 0.269)$, find the equation of the regression line in the above form, giving the coefficients to 3 significant figures.

(You may use $\sum y = 1.641$) [L]

11 A farm food supplier monitors the number of hens kept, x, against the weekly consumption of food, y kg, for a sample of 10 smallholdings.
The results are summarised below.

$$\sum x = 360, \quad \sum x^2 = 17\,362, \quad \sum y = 286$$
$$\sum y^2 = 10\,928.94, \quad \sum xy = 13\,773.6$$

(a) Obtain the regression equation for y on x in the form $y = a + bx$.

(b) Give a practical interpretation of the slope b.

(c) If food costs £7.50 for a 25 kg bag, estimate the weekly cost of feeding the 48 hens. [L]

12 In a chemical reaction it is known that the amount, A grams, of a certain compound produced is a linear function of the temperature, T degrees Celsius. Eight trial runs of this reaction are performed, two at each of four different temperatures. The observed values of A are subject to error. The results are shown.

T	10	15	20	25
A	10 12	15 12	18 16	16 20

Draw a scatter diagram for these data.
Calculate the means of A and T.
Obtain the equation of the regression line of A on T, giving the coefficients to two decimal places.
Draw this line on your scatter diagram.
Use the regression equation to obtain an estimate of the mean value of A when $T = 20$, and explain why this estimate is preferable to averaging the two observed values of A when $T = 20$.
Estimate the mean increase in A for a one degree increase in temperature.
State any reservations you would have about estimating A when $T = 0$. [L]

SUMMARY OF KEY POINTS

1 Explanatory or independent variable: this is the variable that is set independently of the other variable. It is always plotted horizontally.

2 Response or dependent variable: this is the variable whose values are decided by the values of the explanatory or independent variable.

3 Linear regression model: $y_1 = \alpha + \beta x_i + \varepsilon_i$, where $\varepsilon_i \sim N(0, \sigma^2)$.

4 The regression line of y on x is:

$$y = \hat{\alpha} + \hat{\beta}x,$$

where $\hat{\beta} = \dfrac{S_{xy}}{S_{xx}}$ and $\hat{\alpha} = \bar{y} - \hat{\beta}\bar{x}$

Goodness of fit and contingency tables

5

5.1 Forming a hypothesis

Suppose you take a die and throw it 120 times so that the number of throws $N = 120$. If the die is *unbiased* you would in theory expect each of the numbers 1 to 6 to appear 20 times. In other words, you would expect the frequencies of the numbers to fit a discrete uniform distribution with the probability that x takes the value n ($\mathrm{P}(x = n)$) being $\frac{1}{6}$ for $n = 1, 2, \ldots, 6$. The expected frequencies would each be $\mathrm{P}(x = n) \times N = \frac{1}{6} \times 120 = 20$. Since you are taking a sample, it would be surprising if the observed frequency for each number were exactly 20. Suppose now the die was *biased*, again you would not expect the observed frequency of each number to be exactly 20.

You might get results like these:

Number, n	1	2	3	4	5	6
Observed frequency of n	23	15	25	18	21	18

How can you tell if the die is biased? Could you get these results if the die were unbiased, or, to put this in mathematical language, 'does the evidence given by these observed frequencies support the hypothesis that these frequencies do not differ from those you would expect from a discrete uniform distribution?'

You can form a **hypothesis** that the *observed distribution does not differ from a theoretical one*. Because this assumes no difference it is called the **null hypothesis**. The **alternative hypothesis** is that the observed distribution *does differ from the theoretical one.*

There are many experiments in which you may wish to test if the distribution with **observed frequencies** $(\boldsymbol{O_i})$, can be modelled by a particular distribution with **expected frequencies** $(\boldsymbol{E_i})$.

The hypothesis test that we use is:

H_0: there is *no difference* between the observed and the theoretical distribution.

H_1: there *is a difference* between them.

The next question we have to deal with is *how closely* the model fits the observed results. This is called the **goodness of fit** between the observed frequencies and the expected frequencies.

5.2 Goodness of fit

The measure used for goodness of fit may best be understood by looking at an example. Taking the results of the experiment with a die, and adding the expected frequencies, you get:

Number on die, n	1	2	3	4	5	6
Observed frequency, O_i	23	15	25	18	21	18
Expected frequency, E_i	20	20	20	20	20	20

You can show this as a bar chart:

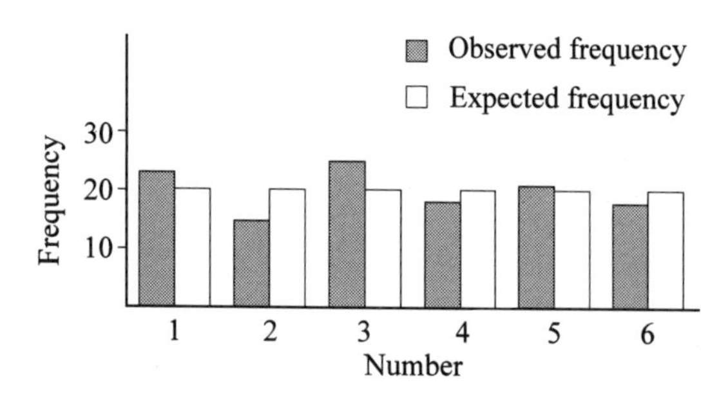

The thing you instinctively look at is the difference between the observed and the expected values. If you add all the differences together you get

$$\sum_{i=1}^{6}(O_i - E_i) = 3 - 5 + 5 - 2 + 1 - 2 = 0$$

The summation comes to zero because both the expected and observed frequencies have to add up to 120. The sum of the differences will *always* be zero no matter how large the individual deviations might be.

You could square the differences and get:

$$\sum_{i=1}^{6}(O_i - E_i)^2$$

This would always give a positive number that would get larger as the differences between the observed and the expected frequencies get larger, and smaller as the differences get smaller. There is, however, an objection to the use of the sum of the squares of the differences. Suppose that you have a difference of 2 between one of the observed frequencies and the related expected frequency.

If the expected frequency is 20 (observed 18) then

$$(O_i - E_i)^2 = (18 - 20)^2 = -2^2 = 4$$

Now if you had done 600 throws of the die, the expected frequencies would each be

$$\frac{600}{6} = 100$$

Supose you again have a difference of 2 between one of the observed and expected frequencies. If the expected frequency is 100 (observed 98) then

$$(O_i - E_i)^2 = (98 - 100)^2 = -2^2 = 4$$

A difference of 2 in an expected frequency of 100 is only 2% of that expected frequency, while a difference of 2 in an expected frequency of 20 would have been $(\frac{2}{20} \times 100\%) = 10\%$. Clearly a 10% difference from the expected frequency is more significant than a 2% difference, yet both would add $2^2 = 4$ to $\sum(O_i - E_i)^2$. If you used $\sum(O_i - E_i)^2$ as a measure of goodness of fit the 2% difference would be treated as being the same as the 10% difference. What is important is not the size of the squared difference but the size of the squared difference *in relation to the expected frequency*. To overcome this problem each $(O_i - E_i)^2$ is divided by E_i. Thus:

If the expected frequency is 20 (observed 18) then

$$\frac{(O_i - E_i)^2}{E_i} = \frac{4}{20} = 0.2$$

If the expected frequency is 100 (observed 98) then

$$\frac{(O_i - E_i)^2}{E_i} = \frac{4}{100} = 0.04$$

You can make a measure of goodness of fit by summing $\frac{(O_i - E_i)^2}{E_i}$. The measure becomes:

$$X^2 = \sum_{i=1}^{n} \frac{(O_i - E_i)^2}{E_i}$$

where the O_i are the observed frequencies and the E_i are the expected frequencies. (The symbol X^2 is used rather than just X to show that the value is never going to be negative.)

You can see at this stage that if there is a perfect fit between all the observed and all the expected values then $O_i - E_i = 0$ for each i, $i = 1$ to n, $\frac{(O_i - E_i)^2}{E_i} = 0$ for each i, and $X^2 = 0$.

If there is not a perfect fit then $(O_i - E_i)^2 > 0$ for one or more i, $i = 1$ to n, $\sum \frac{(O_i - E_i)^2}{E_i} > 0$ and $X^2 > 0$. The less good the fit, the greater the value of X^2.

5.3 Degrees of freedom

We have already pointed out that with 120 tosses of thc die, the expected and observed frequencies both have to add up to 120. The last frequency is decided by the values of the other frequencies. If the first five values are 20 the last value must also be 20 in order to make the totals agree. In our example of the die there are six expected frequencies, but only five that may be set independently. The number of free choices you can make in the allocation of the expected frequencies is called the **number of degrees of freedom**.

The requirement that the totals have to agree is called a **constraint**. We have therefore $6 - 1 = 5$ degrees of freedom, and one constraint.

The number of constraints will depend on the distribution and whether you know the distribution parameters or not. If you do not know a parameter you have to estimate it from the observed data. With every distribution one constraint is given by the need for the sum of the expected frequencies to equal that of the observed frequencies, as in the above example. Every parameter that has to be estimated from the observed data adds a further constraint. This is because the parameter has been found by using that data, and so an estimated value in one of the cells of the table may be found by using that parameter and working backwards. This reduces by one the number of free choices you can make in allocating the observed frequencies, and adds a further constraint. (A known parameter is not determined in any way by the sample values so cannot be used to fix one of them.)

It is usual to refer to each rectangle of a table that contains a piece of data as a cell. You sometimes have to combine frequencies from different cells of the table in order to make the frequencies greater than 5. (The reason for this is given in the next section.) If cells are combined in this way then you have less expected values, and when you calculate the number of degrees of freedom you have to count the number of cells after any such combination and subtract from this the number of constraints.

- **The number of degrees of freedom = number of cells (after any combining) − number of constraints.**

5.4 The chi-squared (χ^2) family of distributions

The χ^2 (pronounced kye-squared) family of distributions can be used as approximations for the statistic X^2.

- $$X^2 = \sum \frac{(O-E)^2}{E} \sim \chi^2$$

X^2 is approximated well by χ^2 *so long as none of the expected values* (E_i) *fall below 5*. If the expected values are less than 5 then you have to combine frequencies in the data table until the frequency is greater than 5. Usually frequencies adjacent to each other in the table are joined together because if one value is low the next one is also likely to be low as well. (This may be seen in examples 2 and 3.)

The diagram below shows some of the members of the χ^2 family of distributions.

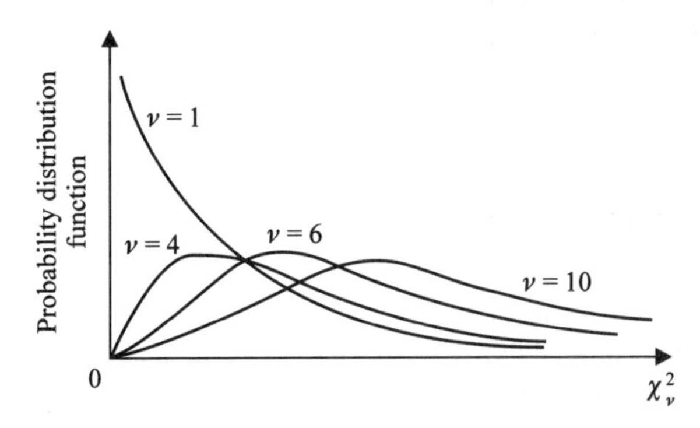

The χ^2 family of distributions is a theoretical one with a probability density function given by

$$f(x) = k_\nu (\tfrac{1}{2}x)^{\frac{1}{2}\nu - 1} e^{-\frac{1}{2}x}, \quad x > 0$$

You need not remember this function, just notice that each member of the family is characterised by the parameter ν (nu), which takes integer values, and the constant k_ν whose value depends on ν. The graphs above were plotted using values generated by this function with $\nu = 1, 4, 6$ and 10. Each value produces a different distribution within the χ^2 family but the values of ν remains constant within any one distribution.

To distinguish which member of the family of distributions you are talking about you write χ^2_ν. Thus χ^2_4 is the χ^2 distribution with $\nu = 4$.

The χ^2 family have distributions which are characterised by the value of ν. The value of X^2 is calculated for a distribution with a certain number of degrees of freedom. When selecting which of the χ^2 family to use as an approximation for X^2 you select the distribution which has ν **equal to the number of degrees of freedom** of your expected values.

5.5 Testing your hypotheses

You began this chapter by forming a hypothesis that there was no difference between the observed and the theoretical distributions. You next found a measure of goodness of fit. The question which arises is, 'could the value of $\sum \frac{(O - E)^2}{E}$ calculated for your sample come from a population for which $\sum \frac{(O - E)^2}{E}$ is equal to zero?'
As in chapter 2 you will only reject the null hypothesis if by accepting the alternative hypothesis you have only a small chance of being wrong. Typically this figure is set at 5%. To find the value of $\sum \frac{(O - E)^2}{E}$ that is only exceded with probability of 5% (the critical value), we use the appropriate χ^2 distribution.
For a given value of ν, the critical value which is exceeded with probability 5% is written $\chi^2_\nu(5\%)$ or $\chi^2_\nu(0.05)$.

Table 5 on page 208 gives you, for each value of ν, critical values of χ^2_ν for probabilities of 99.5%, 99%, 97.5%, 95%, and 90% (0.995, 0.99, 0.975, 0.95 and 0.9), and 10%, 5%, 2.5%, 1% and 0.5% (0.1, 0.05, 0.025, 0.01 and 0.005). (You will only be concerned with the values between 10% and 0.5% in this book.)

For example, with $\nu = 5$ the value of χ^2 that is exceeded with 0.05 probability ($\chi_5^2(5\%)$), is 11.070. This is shown on the probability diagram below.

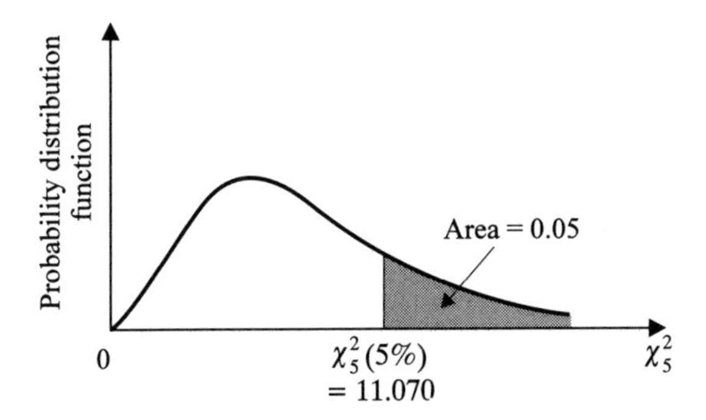

Also from the table, $\chi_5^2(10\%) = 9.236$, $\chi_5^2(2.5\%) = 12.832$, $\chi_5^2(1\%) = 15.086$ and $\chi_5^2(0.5\%) = 16.750$. For each other value of ν the critical values may be looked up in the same way.

Remember X^2 is approximated well by χ^2 so long as *none of the expected values* (E_i) *fall below 5*.

Let's go back to the die problem. If you set hypotheses:

H_0: The observed distribution does not differ from the theoretical one (the die is not biased).

H_1: The observed distribution does differ from the theoretical one (the die is biased).

From Table 5 the critical value of χ^2 is 11.070 at the 5% level ($\chi_5^2(5\%) = 11.070$).

In this case you can calculate $\sum \frac{(O_i - E_i)^2}{E_i}$ as follows:

Number	1	2	3	4	5	6
O_i	23	15	25	18	21	18
E_i	20	20	20	20	20	20
$\frac{(O_i - E_i)^2}{E_i}$	0.45	1.25	1.25	0.2	0.05	0.2

$$\sum \frac{(O_i - E_i)^2}{E_i} = 3.4$$

Since $3.4 < 11.070$ you do not reject the null hypothesis at the 0.05 level: there is not enough evidence to suggest the die is biased.

5.6 The general method for testing the goodness of fit

1. Determine which distribution is likely to be a good model by examining the conditions applying to the observed data (the necessary conditions were given in Book T1).
2. Estimate parameters (if necessary) from your observed data.
3. Calculate estimated frequencies.
4. Combine any expected frequencies so that none are less than 5.
5. Find ν using ν = number of cells after combining – number of restraints.
6. Find the critical value of χ^2 from the table.
7. Calculate $\sum \frac{(O_i - E_i)^2}{E_i}$
8. See if your value is significant.
9. Draw the appropriate conclusion and interpret in the context of the original problem.

5.7 Applying goodness-of-fit tests when the data are discrete

You met three discrete distributions in Book T1. The conditions under which each distribution arises, and the methods used in their calculation are repeated here for easy reference. You will also see how to use them as models for observed distributions.

Testing a discrete uniform distribution as a model

You have already seen an example of this. The conditions under which a discrete distribution arises are

- The discrete random variable X is defined over a set of k distinct values.
- Each value is equally likely.

The probability of each value is given by

$$\mathrm{P}(X = x_r) = \frac{1}{k}, \quad r = 1, 2, \ldots, k$$

The frequencies for a sample size of N are given by

$$\text{Frequency} = P(X = x_r) \times N = \frac{1}{k} \times N = \frac{N}{k} \text{ for } r = 1, 2, \ldots, k$$

Since a uniform distribution has only the restriction that the expected frequencies add up to N, the degrees of freedom ν = number of cells − 1.

Example 1

100 random digits between 0 and 9 are selected from a table with the frequencies shown below.

Digit	0	1	2	3	4	5	6	7	8	9
Frequency	11	8	8	7	8	9	12	9	13	15

Could the digits be from a random number table? Test at the 0.05 level.

H_0: The digits are random.
H_1: The digits are not random.

Each digit should have an equal chance of selection, so the appropriate model is the discrete uniform distribution.

$$P(X = x_r) = \tfrac{1}{10} \quad r = 0, 1, \ldots, 9$$

Digit	0	1	2	3	4	5	6	7	8	9
Observed, O_i	11	8	8	7	8	9	12	9	13	15
Expected, E_i	10	10	10	10	10	10	10	10	10	10
$\frac{(O_i - E_i)^2}{E_i}$	0.1	0.4	0.4	0.9	0.4	0.1	0.4	0.1	0.9	2.5

$$\sum \frac{(O_i - E_i)^2}{E_i} = 6.2$$

The number of degrees of freedom is:

$$y = 10 - 1 = 9$$

From Table 5 $\qquad \chi_9^2(5\%) = 16.919$

So: $\qquad \sum \frac{(O_i - E_i)^2}{E_i} < 16.919$

You do not reject H_0: there is no evidence to suggest the digits are not random.

Testing a binomial distribution as a model

The conditions under which a binomial distribution arises are:

- There must be a fixed number (n) of trials in each observation.
- The trials must be independent.
- The trials have only two outcomes: success and failure.
- The probability of success (p) is constant.

For a binomial

$$P(X = r) = \binom{n}{r} p^r (1-p)^{n-r} \quad r = 0, 1, 2, \ldots, n$$

The frequency f_r with which each r occurs when the number of observations is N is given by

$$f_r = P(X = r) \times N$$

The binomial distribution has two parameters, n and p. n gives the usual restriction that the expected frequencies have to have the same total as observed frequencies, while p may be known or it may be estimated from the observed values, by using frequencies of success.

$$p = \frac{\text{total number of successes}}{\text{number of trials} \times N} = \frac{\sum(r \times f_r)}{n \times N}$$

If p is not estimated: $\nu = \text{number of cells} - 1$

If p is estimated: $\nu = \text{number of cells} - 2$

Example 2

The data in the table are thought to be modelled by a binomial B(10, 0.2). Use the table for the binomial cumulative distribution function to find expected values, and conduct a test to see if this is a good model. Use a 5% significance level.

x	0	1	2	3	4	5	6	7	8
Frequency of x	12	28	28	17	7	4	2	2	0

H_0: The results can be modelled by a B(10, 0.2) distribution.
H_1: The results cannot be modelled by a B(10, 0.2) distribution.

From the table of the binomial cumulative distribution function (Table 1) you get the following probabilities, and by multiplying by 100 (sum of observed frequencies) you get the expected frequencies.

The last one can be found by taking the sum of the rest from 100 (100–99.99), since the sum has to come to 100. This gives one constraint on the degree of freedom.

x	0	1	2	3	4	5	6	7	8
Probability of x	0.1074	0.2684	0.3020	0.2013	0.0881	0.0264	0.0055	0.0008	0.0001
Expected frequency of x	10.74	26.84	30.2	20.13	8.81	2.64	0.55	0.08	0.01

You will have to combine the last five cells in the table in order to get all the expected frequencies greater than 5.

The observed and expected frequencies are shown together in the table below.

O_i	12	28	28	17	15
E_i	10.74	26.84	30.2	20.13	12.09
$\frac{(O_i - E_i)^2}{E_i}$	0.1478	0.0501	0.1603	0.4867	0.7004

$$\sum \frac{(O_i - E_i)^2}{E_i} = 1.545$$

The number of degrees of freedom = number of cells after combining $-1 = 5 - 1 = 4$

From Table 5 the critical value $\chi_4^2(5\%)$ is 9.488.

You do not reject H_0: B(10,0.2) is a possible model for these data.

Example 3

A study of the number of girls in families with five children was done upon 100 such families. The results are summarised in the following table.

Number of girls (r)	0	1	2	3	4	5
Frequency (f)	13	18	38	20	10	1

It is suggested that the distribution may be modelled by a binomial distribution.

(a) Give reasons why this might be so.
(b) Test to see if the binomial distribution is a good model.

(a) There is a fixed number of children in the family so $n = 5$. The trials are independent (assume no multiple births). There are two outcomes to each trial: success (a girl), failure (a boy).

(b) H_0: The distribution of girls in these families is binomial.
H_1: It is not binomial.

Before calculating the expected frequencies you need to find the probability of success (p). The number of observations $N = 100$, the number of trials $n = 5$.

If you use the data to estimate p, then

$$p = \frac{\sum(r \times f_r)}{100n} = \frac{199}{100 \times 5} = 0.398$$

(and the constraints are 2).

If you assume that a girl is as likely as a boy then you do not have to estimate p since you know that $p = 0.5$, and, since p is not estimated, ν is decreased by only 1.

Let us assume that $p = 0.5$, then your hypotheses become:

H_0: B(5,0.5) (a binomial with $n = 5$ and $p = 0.5$) is a suitable model
H_1: B(5,0.5) is not a suitable model.

Since $n = 5$ you could use the table for a binomial distribution to find the probabilities for each value of r, but here they are calculated so that you may see the method to use if n is not in the table.

r	P(r)	*Expected frequency* 100P(r)
0	$(0.5)^5 = 0.031\,25$	3.125
1	$5(0.5)^4(0.5)^1 = 0.156\,25$	15.625
2	$\frac{5 \times 4}{2}(0.5)^3(0.5)^2 = 0.3125$	31.25
3	$\frac{5 \times 4 \times 3}{3 \times 2}(0.5)^2(0.5)^3 = 0.3125$	31.25
4	$\frac{5 \times 4 \times 3 \times 2}{4 \times 3 \times 2}(0.5)^1(0.5)^4 = 0.156\,25$	15.625
5	$\frac{5 \times 4 \times 3 \times 2 \times 1}{5 \times 4 \times 3 \times 2}(0.5)^0(0.5)^5 = 0.03125$	3.125

Since 3.125 < 5 you must combine cells:

r	O_i	E_i	$\frac{(O_i - E_i)^2}{E_i}$
0 or 1	31	18.75	8.003
2	38	31.25	1.458
3	20	31.25	4.05
4 or 5	11	18.75	3.203

$$\sum \frac{(O_i - E_i)^2}{E_i} = 16.714$$

You have $4 - 1 = 3$ degrees of freedom.

From the tables: $\chi_3^2(0.05) = 7.815$

so: $\sum \frac{(O_i - E_i)^2}{E_i} > 7.815$

You reject H_0: the number of girls in families with five children does not in this case fit a binomial distribution with $n = 5$ and $p = 0.5$.

You could try to refine your model by using the data and seeing if B(5,0.398) is a better model. The hypotheses are the same but the model is new. The new expected data can be calculated as before.

r	P(r)	E
0	$(0.602)^5 = 0.0791$	7.91
1	$5(0.602)^4(0.398) = 0.2614$	26.14
2	$10(0.602)^3(0.398)^2 = 0.3456$	34.56
3	$10(0.602)^2(0.398)^3 = 0.2285$	22.85
4	$5(0.602)^1(0.398)^4 = 0.0755$	7.55
5	$(0.398)^5 = 0.0099$	0.99

You have to combine cells to give expected frequencies greater than 5:

r	O_i	E_i	$\frac{(O_i - E_i)^2}{E_i}$
0	13	7.91	3.2753
1	18	26.14	2.5347
2	38	34.56	0.3424
3	20	22.85	0.3555
>3	11	8.54	0.7086

$$\sum \frac{(O_i - E_i)^2}{E_i} = 7.2165$$

There are $5 - 2 = 3$ degrees of freedom (you have gained one cell but have one more constraint). As before the critical value is 7.815. You do not reject H_0: B(5,0.398) is a more suitable model.

Testing a Poisson distribution as a model

The conditions under which a Poisson distribution is likely to arise are:

- The N events occur *independently* of each other.
- The events occur *singly* in continuous space or time.
- The events occur at a *constant rate*, in the sense that the mean number in an interval is proportional to the length of the interval.
- The mean and the variance are *equal.*

For a Poisson distribution with mean λ

$$P(X = r) = \frac{e^{-\lambda}\lambda^r}{r!} \qquad r = 0, 1, 2, 3, \ldots$$

Although, theoretically, r has an infinite number of integer values, in practice all those greater than or equal to some number n are put together and the probability $P(X \geqslant n)$ is found from:

$$P(X \geqslant n) = 1 - P(X < n)$$

You choose n equal to the highest value of r for which the observed frequency is >0. In example 4, n is chosen to be 7 since all telephone calls for $r \geqslant 8$ have zero frequencies.

The frequency f_r with which each r occurs is given by $P(X = r) \times N$.

The Poisson distribution has a single parameter λ, which may be known or which may be estimated from the observed data using:

$$\lambda = \frac{\sum(r \times f_r)}{N}$$

There is the usual restriction on the total of the expected frequencies being equal to the total of the observed frequencies.

If λ is not estimated: ν = number of cells − 1

If λ is estimated: ν = number of cells − 2

Example 4

The numbers of telephone calls arriving at an exchange in six-minute periods were recorded over a period of 8 hours, with the following results.

Number of calls, r	0	1	2	3	4	5	6	7	8
Frequency, f_r	8	19	26	13	7	5	1	1	0

Can these results be modelled by a Poisson distribution?

H_0: The calls follow a Poisson distribution Po(λ).
H_1: The calls do not follow a Poisson distribution.

Since you do not know the value of λ you must estimate it from the observed frequencies.

$$\text{Total number of observations} = N = \frac{8 \times 60}{6} = 80$$

$$\lambda = \frac{\sum(r \times f_r)}{N} = \frac{176}{80} = 2.2$$

r	$P(X = r)$	*Expected frequency of r*
0	$\frac{e^{-2.2} \times 2.2^0}{1} = 0.1108$	8.864 (0.1108 × 80)
1	$\frac{e^{-2.2} \times 2.2^1}{1} = 0.2438$	19.504
2	$\frac{e^{-2.2} \times 2.2^2}{2} = 0.2681$	21.448
3	$\frac{e^{-2.2} \times 2.2^3}{3 \times 2} = 0.1966$	15.728
4	$\frac{e^{-2.2} \times 2.2^4}{4 \times 3 \times 2} = 0.1082$	8.656
5	$\frac{e^{-2.2} \times 2.2^5}{5 \times 4 \times 3 \times 2} = 0.0476$	3.808
6	$\frac{e^{-2.2} \times 2.2^6}{6 \times 5 \times 4 \times 3 \times 2} = 0.0174$	1.392
7 or more	$1 - 0.9925$	0.6

The value of $P(r = 7$ or more) is obtained by subtracting the sum of the other probability values from 1.

In this case you have to combine cells to give expected frequencies of more than 5:

r	O_i	E_i	$\dfrac{(O_i - E_i)^2}{E_i}$
0	8	8.864	0.0842
1	19	19.504	0.0130
2	26	21.448	0.9661
3	13	15.728	0.4732
4	7	8.656	0.3168
5 or more	7	5.8	0.2483

$$\sum \frac{(O_i - E_i)^2}{E_i} = 2.1016$$

You have $6 - 2 = 4$ degrees of freedom, since λ was estimated from the observed frequencies.

From the χ^2 table (Table 5) $\chi_4^2(5\%) = 9.488$

$$\sum \frac{(O_i - E_i)^2}{E_i} < 9.488$$

So you have no evidence to reject H_0. The calls can be modelled by a Po(2.2) distribution.

Exercise 5A

1 The following table shows observed values for what is thought to be a discrete uniform distribution.

x	1	2	3	4	5	6	7	8
Frequency of x	12	24	18	20	25	17	21	23

(a) Calculate the expected frequencies and, using a 5% significance level, conduct a goodness of fit test.

(b) State your conclusions.

2 The following tables show observed values (O) and expected values (E) for a goodness of fit test of a binomial distribution model. The probability used in calculating the expected values has not been found from the observed values.

O	17	28	32	15	5	3
E	19.69	34.74	27.59	12.98	4.01	0.99

(a) Conduct the test using a 5% significance level and state your conclusions.

(b) Suggest how the model might be improved.

3 The following table shows observed values for a distribution which it is thought may be modelled by a Poisson distribution.

x	0	1	2	3	4	5	>5
Frequency of x	12	23	24	24	12	5	0

A possible model is thought to be Po(2). From tables the expected values are found to be as shown in the following table.

x	0	1	2	3	4	5	>5
Expected frequency of x	13.53	27.07	27.07	18.04	9.02	3.61	1.66

(a) Conduct a goodness of fit test at the 5% significance level.

(b) It is suggested that the model could be improved by estimating the value of λ from the observed results. What effect would this have on the number of constraints placed upon the degrees of freedom?

4 A mail order firm receives packets every day through the mail. They think that their deliveries are uniformly distributed throughout the week. Test this assertion, given that their deliveries over a 4-week period were as follows. Use a 0.05 significance level.

Day	Mon	Tues	Wed	Thurs	Fri	Sat
Frequency	15	23	19	20	14	11

5 Over a period of 50 weeks the number of road accidents reported to a police station were as shown.

Number of accidents	0	1	2	3	4
Number of weeks	15	13	9	13	0

(a) Find the mean number of accidents per week.

(b) Using this mean and a 0.10 significance level, test the assertion that these data are from a population with a Poisson distribution.

6 A marksman fires 6 shots at a target and records the number r of bull's-eyes hit. After a series of 100 such trials he analyses his scores, the frequencies being as follows.

r	0	1	2	3	4	5	6
Frequency	0	26	36	20	10	6	2

(a) Estimate the probability of hitting a bull's-eye.

(b) Use a test at the 0.05 significance level to see if these results are consistent with the assumption of a binomial distribution.

7 The table below shows the number of employees in thousands at five factories and the number of accidents in 3 years.

Factory	A	B	C	D	E
Employees (thousands)	4	3	5	1	2
Accidents	22	14	25	8	12

Using a 0.05 level significance, test the hypothesis that the number of accidents per 1000 employees is constant at each factory.

8 In a test to determine the red blood cell count in a patient's blood sample, the number of cells in each of 80 squares is counted with the following results.

Number of cells per square, x	0	1	2	3	4	5	6	7	8
Frequency, f	2	8	15	18	14	13	7	3	0

It is assumed that these will fit a Poisson distribution. Test this assertion at the 0.05 significance level.

9 A factory has a machine. The number of times it broke down each week was recorded over 100 weeks with the following results.

Number of times broken down	0	1	2	3	4	5
Frequency	50	24	12	9	5	0

It is thought that the distribution is Poisson.

(a) Give reasons why this assumption might be made.

(b) Conduct a test at the 0.05 level of significance to see if the assumption is reasonable.

10 In a lottery there are 505 prizes, and it is assumed that they will be uniformly distributed throughout the numbered tickets. An investigation gave the following:

Ticket number	1– 1000	1001–2000	2001–3000	3001–4000	4001–5000	5001–6000	6001–7000	7001–8000	8001–9000	9001–10 000
Frequency	56	49	35	47	63	58	44	52	51	50

Using a suitable test with a 0.05 significance level, and stating your null and alternative hypotheses, see if the assumption is reasonable.

5.8 Applying goodness-of-fit tests to continuous distributions

When dealing with continuous data you have to group the values into classes and then observe the frequency for each class. There are two common ways of indicating the classes:

(i)

5–9	10–14	15–19

For this method you will have to find the real class intervals. These are 4.5 to 9.5, 9.5 to 14.5, and so on.

(ii)

10–	20–	30–

This is another way of writing 10– < 20, 20– < 30 and so on. The class intervals are 10 to 20, 20 to 30 and so on.

Again, conditions under which each arises and the methods used in calculation are given for ease of reference.

Testing a normal distribution as a model

The indicators which show that a normal distribution might be expected are:

- the distribution is 'bell shaped' and is symmetrical about the mean.
- approximately two-thirds of the values fall within one standard deviation of the mean.

If a continuous random variable has a normal distribution it has a probability distribution function

$$f(x) = \frac{1}{\sigma\sqrt{(2\pi)}} e^{-(x-\mu)^2/2\sigma^2}$$

The normal distribution has two parameters, μ and σ, which may be known or which may have to be estimated from the observations. The best estimates for μ and σ^2 are $\bar{x}$ and s^2.

$$\bar{x} = \frac{\sum x_i}{n} \quad \text{and} \quad s^2 = \frac{\sum(x_i - \bar{x})^2}{n-1}$$

where n is the total number of observations. (If the individual values of x are not known you use the mean value of the group in which they fall.)

If the parameters are not estimated:

$$\nu = \text{number of cells after combining} - 1$$

If both the parameters are estimated:

$$\nu = \text{number of cells after combining} - 3$$

If one parameter only is estimated:

$$\nu = \text{number of cells after combining} - 2$$

Because the normal distribution is continuous you can only conduct the test if your observations are collected together in class intervals, and you look at the frequency of occurrence within each class interval. If X is a variable then you will wish to know for each class $P(a \leqslant X < b)$ where a and b are the real class boundaries. The normal distribution stretches from $-\infty$ to $+\infty$ so the end groups will be of the form $X \leqslant b$ at the bottom and $X \geqslant a$ at the top when calculating probabilities.

You obtain the probabilities from the normal distribution table of $N(0,1^2)$ using:

$$\begin{aligned}P(a < X < b) &= P\left(\frac{a-\mu}{\sigma} < Z < \frac{b-\mu}{\sigma}\right)\\ &= \Phi\left(\frac{b-\mu}{\sigma}\right) - \Phi\left(\frac{a-\mu}{\sigma}\right)\end{aligned}$$

This was explained in chapter 8 of Book T1.

The class frequencies are obtained by multiplying the probabilities by n.

Example 5

During observations on the height of 200 male students the following data were observed.

Height (cm)	150–154	155–159	160–164	165–169	170–174	175–179	180–184	185–189	190–194
Frequency	4	6	12	30	64	52	18	10	4

(a) Test at the 0.05 level to see if the height of male students could be modelled by a normal distribution with mean 172 and standard deviation 6.

(b) Describe how you would modify this test if the mean and variance were unknown.

(a) H_0: The normal distribution N(172,36) is a suitable model.
H_1: The normal distribution N(172,36) is not a suitable model.

Before calculating the expected frequencies by using $f_r = P(a \leqslant X < b) \times n$ with $n = 200$, you must find the true class boundaries and convert these to Z values using $\mu = 172$ and $\sigma = 6$. You begin as you did in Book T1 with a diagram to show the areas to be found:

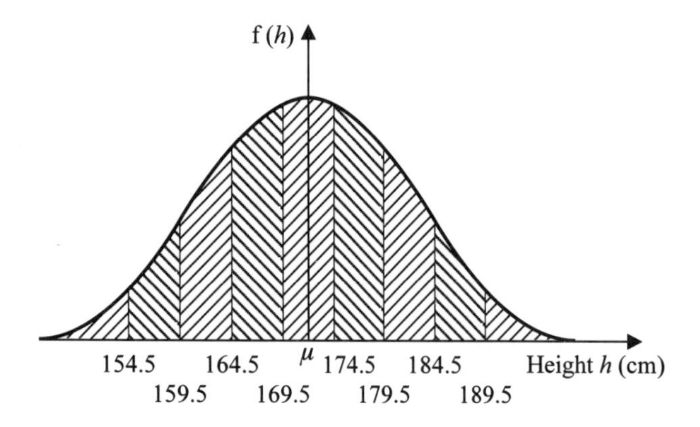

Classes a b	$\frac{b-\mu}{\sigma}$	$P(a \leqslant X < b)$ $= \Phi\left(\frac{b-\mu}{\sigma}\right) - \Phi\left(\frac{a-\mu}{\sigma}\right)$	*Frequencies* $P(a \leqslant X < b) \times n$
< 154.5	−2.9167	0.0018 − 0.0000 = 0.0018	0.36
154.5–159.5	−2.0833	0.0187 − 0.0018 = 0.0169	3.38
159.5–164.5	−1.25	0.1056 − 0.0187 = 0.0869	17.38
164.5–169.5	−0.4167	0.3384 − 0.1056 = 0.2328	46.56
169.5–174.5	0.4167	0.6616 − 0.3384 = 0.3232	64.64
174.5–179.5	1.25	0.8944 − 0.6616 = 0.2328	46.56
179.5–184.5	2.0833	0.9813 − 0.8944 = 0.0869	17.38
184.5–189.5	2.9167	0.9982 − 0.9813 = 0.0169	3.38
> 189.5		1.0000 − 0.9982 = 0.0018	0.36

You must combine frequencies less than 5:

Class	O_i	E_i	$\frac{(O_i - E_i)^2}{E_i}$
150–164	22	21.12	0.0367
165–169	30	46.56	5.8899
170–174	64	64.64	0.0063
175–179	52	46.56	0.6356
180–194	32	21.12	5.6048

$$\sum \frac{(O_i - E_i)^2}{E_i} = 12.1733$$

Since μ and σ are not estimated:

$$\text{degrees of freedom} = 5 - 1 = 4$$

From the tables the critical values $\chi_4^2(0.05) = 9.488$

$$\sum \frac{(O_i - E_i)^2}{E_i} > 9.488$$

You reject H_0: the normal distribution N(173,36) is *not* a suitable model.

The expected values in this example have been calculated using the normal table. Where the value of z falls between two values in the table interpolation has been used. The method for doing this is described in Book T1. Some calculators will give this reading directly. In your examination you will not be penalised if you use the nearest value to z in the table rather than interpolating.

(b) You would estimate the parameters as follows.

$$\bar{x} = \frac{152 \times 4 + 157 \times 6 + 162 \times 12 + 167 \times 30 + 172 \times 64 + 177 \times 52 + 182 \times 18 + 187 \times 10 + 192 \times 4}{200}$$

$$= 173.15$$

$$\begin{aligned} s^2 &= [(152 - 173.15)^2 \times 4 + (157 - 173.15)^2 \times 6 + (162 - 173.15)^2 \times 12 + (167 - 173.15)^2 \times 30 \\ &\quad + (172 - 173.15)^2 \times 64 + (177 - 173.15)^2 \times 52 + (182 - 173.15)^2 \times 18 \\ &\quad + (187 - 173.15)^2 \times 10 + (192 - 173.15)^2 \times 4] \div 199 \\ &= 58.22 \\ s &= 7.63 \end{aligned}$$

The test would be conducted with $5 - 3 = 2$ degrees of freedom.

Testing a continuous uniform distribution as a model

The indicators that show that a continuous uniform distribution might be expected are:

- symmetry about the mean
- classes of equal width have equal probabilities.

A random variable X having a uniform distribution over the interval (α, β) has a probability distribution function

$$f(x) = \begin{cases} \dfrac{1}{\beta - \alpha} & \alpha < x < \beta \\ 0 \text{ otherwise} \end{cases}$$

Because of the continuous nature of the distribution you must collect your observations into n non-overlapping classes. You therefore will be looking at probabilities such as $p(a < X < b)$ where $a \geqslant \alpha$ and $b \leqslant \beta$. The probabilities may be calculated using

$$P(a < X < b) = \frac{b - a}{\beta - \alpha}$$

The continuous uniform distribution only has the requirement that the expected frequencies must equal the observed frequencies. Thus $\nu =$ number of cells $- 1$.

Example 6

In a study on the habits of a flock of starlings, the direction in which they headed when they left their roost in the mornings was recorded over 240 days. The direction was found by recording if they headed between certain features of the landscape. The compass bearings of these features were then measured. The results are given below.

Direction (degrees)	0–58	58–100	100–127	127–190	190–256	256–296	296–360
Frequency	31	40	47	40	32	30	20

It is suggested that they feed equally in all directions. Suggest a suitable model and test to see if these data support this view.

A suitable model would be the continuous uniform distribution because you would expect the distribution to be symmetrical about the mean and classes of equal width would be expected to have equal probabilities.

H_0: The continuous uniform distribution is a suitable model (the starlings feed in all directions).
H_1: It is not a suitable model (they do not feed in all directions).

Class a to b degrees	$b - a$	$P(a < X < b) = \frac{b-a}{360-0}$	*Frequency* $= P(a < X < b) \times n = P(a < X < b) \times 240$
0–58	58	0.1611	38.67
58–100	42	0.1167	28
100–127	27	0.075	18
127–190	63	0.175	42
190–256	66	0.1833	44
256–296	40	0.1111	26.66
296–360	64	0.1778	42.67

Class	O_i	E_i	$\frac{(O_i - E_i)^2}{E_i}$
0–58	31	38.67	1.5213
58–100	40	28	5.1429
100–127	47	18	46.7222
127–190	40	42	0.0952
190–256	32	44	3.2727
256–296	30	26.66	0.4184
296–300	20	42.67	12.0442

$$\sum \frac{(O_i - E_i)^2}{E_i} = 69.2169$$

There are $7 - 1 = 6$ degrees of freedom.

From the table $\chi_6^2(0.05) = 12.592$

$$\sum \frac{(O_i - E_i)^2}{E_i} > 12.592$$

You reject H_0 and accept H_1. The continuous uniform distribution is *not* a suitable model. The birds do not feed in all directions. They have preferred feeding areas.

It is clear that in this case the class 100–127 alone gives a significant result, so there is no need to carry on past this point. It also appears that the class 100–127 is more popular than the other classes. You have already discovered something about the birds' habits and you can count this a success. You might, however, like to consider how you would refine this model or what further investigations you could make. What is there about the feeding ground in this direction? What has this direction got in common with the other popular feeding areas? If this sector and its attractions is removed, do the birds feed equally in all directions? Does the direction in which they fly out truly represent their feeding ground?

Exercise 5B

1 Broad beans were grown under controlled conditions for a period of 10 weeks after germination. No measurement of mean height was recorded at the end of week one, but the mean height recorded at the end of each subsequent week was as follows.

Week	2	3	4	5	6	7	8	9	10
Height (cm)	20	31	48	63	75	88	101	112	120

Conduct a goodness of fit test to see if the rate of growth between weeks 2 and 10 can be modelled by a continuous uniform distribution. Use a 5% level of significance.

2 The diameters of a random sample of 30 mass-produced components were measured by checking their diameter with gauges. Of the 30, 18 passed through a 4.0 mm gauge and of these 6 failed to pass through a 3.5 mm gauge. Use χ^2 to test the hypothesis that the diameters of the components were a sample of a normal population with mean 3.8 mm and standard deviation 0.5 mm. Use a 5% significance level for your test.

3 An egg producer takes a sample of 150 eggs from his flock of chickens and grades them into classes according to their weights as follows.

Class	2	3	4	5	6
Weight (g)	66–70	61–65	56–60	51–55	46–50
Frequency	10	32	67	29	12

Does this distribution fit a normal distribution of mean 58 g and standard deviation 4 g? Use a 5% significance level for your test.

4 A sample of 100 apples is taken from a load. The apples have the following distribution of sizes.

Diameter (cm)	$\leqslant 6$	7	8	9	$\geqslant 10$
Frequency	8	29	38	16	9

It is thought that they come from a normal distribution with mean diameter of 8 cm and a standard deviation of 0.9 cm. Test this assertion using a 0.05 level of significance.

5 A shop owner found that the number of cans of a particular drink sold per day during 100 days in summer was as follows.

Drinks per day, d	0–	10–	20–	30–	40–
Frequency of d	10	24	45	14	7

It is thought that these data can be modelled by a normal distribution.

(a) Estimate values of μ and σ and conduct a goodness of fit test using a 1% significance level.

(b) Explain how the shopkeeper might use this model.

6 An outfitter sells boys' raincoats and these are stocked in four sizes.

Size 1 fits boys up to 1.25 m in height. Size 2 fits boy from 1.26 to 1.31 m. Size 3 fits boys from 1.32 to 1.37 m. Size 4 fits those over 1.38 m. To assist the outfitter in deciding the stock levels he should order each year, the heights of 120 boys in the right age range were measured with the following results.

Height, h(m)	1.20–1.22	1.23–1.25	1.26–1.28	1.29–1.31	1.32–1.34	1.35–1.37	1.38–1.40	1.41–1.43
Frequency of h	9	9	18	23	20	19	17	5

It is suggested that a suitable model for these data is N(1.32,0.0016).

(a) Conduct a goodness-of-fit test using a $2\frac{1}{2}\%$ significance level.

(b) Estimate values of μ and σ using the observed values and using these conduct a goodness-of-fit test using a $2\frac{1}{2}\%$ significance level.

(c) Select the best model and use it to tell the outfitter how many of each size should be ordered per year if the normal annual sales are 1200.

7 It is thought that trees growing in the open will have their branches continuously uniformly distributed around their trunks, while those growing at the edge of a wood will not. To test this theory the direction taken by the first five branches coming from a central trunk of a particular species was measured for 100 trees grown well spaced out in a nursery and 100 trees of the same species growing at the southern edge of a wood. The results were as follows:

Direction (degrees)	−45	−90	−135	−180	−225	−270	−315	−360
Frequency in open	60	68	70	61	58	70	63	50
Frequency at edge	43	60	72	80	75	67	63	40

Conduct a goodness-of-fit test at the 5% level to test these theories, and state your conclusions.

5.9 Contingency tables

So far in this chapter you have been concerned with the frequency with which a single event occurs. For example, you might count the number of times each of the numbers 1 to 6 appears when a die is thrown 100 times. The thing looked at in this case is the frequencies with which the numbers 1 to 6 appear. Sometimes you are interested in the frequencies with which two criteria are fulfilled at the same time. If you study the frequency with which A-level Maths passes at grades A, B and C occur you may also be interested in which of two schools the students attended. Here you have two criteria: the pass level and the school. You can show these results by means of a **contingency table**, which shows the frequency with which each of the results occurred at each school separately.

		Pass (criterion 1)			*Totals*
		A	*B*	*C*	
School (criterion 2)	*X*	18	12	20	50
	Y	26	12	32	70
	Totals	44	24	52	120

This is called a **2 × 3** contingency table since there are **two rows** and **three columns**.

You can see that school X had 12 passes at grade B out of a total of 50, and that there was a total of 44 passes at grade A out of 120 when the two schools are combined. The question that arises is, 'Is there any difference between the two schools' sets of results?' You pose the hypothesis 'are the two criteria independent?'

H_0: The criteria are independent. There is no connection between the school and the grades of pass.
H_1: They are not independent. There is a connection.

Now, overall:

$$P(\text{A grade}) = \tfrac{44}{120}$$
$$P(\text{school X}) = \tfrac{50}{120}$$

So

$$P(\text{A grade and school X}) = P(\text{A grade}) \times P(\text{school X}) = \tfrac{44}{120} \times \tfrac{50}{120}$$

if the events are independent.

The expected frequency of passes at A from school X is therefore

$$\tfrac{44}{120} \times \tfrac{50}{120} \times 120 = \frac{44 \times 50}{120} = 18.33$$

Notice that the expected frequency is given by

$$\frac{\text{row total} \times \text{column total}}{\text{grand total}}$$

and is calculated on the assumption that the criteria are independent. You can find the other expected frequencies in the same way.

You can calculate the expected frequencies as in the table below.

		Pass			*Totals*
		A	*B*	*C*	
School	*X*	$\frac{50 \times 44}{120} = 18.33$	$\frac{50 \times 24}{120} = 10$	$\frac{50 \times 52}{120} = 21.67$	50
	Y	$\frac{70 \times 44}{120} = 25.67$	$\frac{70 \times 24}{120} = 14$	$\frac{70 \times 52}{120} = 30.33$	70
	Totals	44	24	52	120

Degrees of freedom

When calculating expected values you need not calculate the last value in each row, because the sum of the values in each row has to equal the row total. For example,

$$P(\text{C grade and school X}) = 50 - (18.33 + 10)$$

In the same way the last value in each of the other rows is fixed by the row total once the other value in the row is known. For example,

$$P(\text{A grade and school Y}) = 44 - 18.33$$

In general, if there are h rows, then once $(h - 1)$ expected frequencies have been calculated the last value in the row is fixed by the row total. If there are k columns, once $(k - 1)$ columns have been calculated the last column value is fixed by the column total.

- **The number of independent variables is given therefore by $(h - 1)(k - 1)$. That is to say,**

$$\nu = (\boldsymbol{h} - \mathbf{1})(\boldsymbol{k} - \mathbf{1})$$

You can now conduct a goodness-of-fit test on these data.

O_i	E_i	$\frac{(O_i - E_i)^2}{E_i}$
18	18.33	0.0059
12	10.00	0.4000
20	21.67	0.1287
26	25.67	0.0042
12	14.00	0.2857
32	30.33	0.0920

$$\sum \frac{(O_i - E_i)^2}{E_i} = 0.9165$$

$\nu = (h - 1)(k - 1) = (2 - 1)(3 - 1) = 2$

From tables the critical value at the 0.05 significance level is 5.991.

$$\sum \frac{(O_i - E_i)^2}{E_i} = 0.9165$$

So: $$\sum \frac{(O_i - E_i)^2}{E_i} < 5.991$$

You do not reject H_0: there is no evidence to suggest a connection between the school and the grades of pass.

5.10 Yates' correction

When dealing with 2×2 contingency tables (2 rows $\times$ 2 columns), the number of degrees of freedom is reduced to 1. In these circumstances the approximation to the continuous χ^2 distribution is improved if **Yates' correction** is applied. The correction is done by subtracting $\frac{1}{2}$ from the magnitude of the difference between the O_i and the E_i. The corrected formula becomes:

■ $$\sum \frac{(|O_i - E_i| - \frac{1}{2})^2}{E_i}$$

Each difference is reduced absolutely by $\frac{1}{2}$. Thus if $O_i - E_i = 4.6$ then

$$|O_i - E_i| - \tfrac{1}{2} = 4.1$$

and if $O_i - E_i = -4.6$ then

$$|O_i - E_i| - \tfrac{1}{2} = 4.1$$

■ **It is particularly important in 2×2 tables that the expected frequencies do not drop below 5, otherwise the approximation of the statistic by χ^2 will no longer hold.**

Example 7

During the trial of a new drug, 60 volunteers out of 200 were treated with the drug. Those experiencing a relief of their symptoms and those who did not were recorded as follows:

	Relief	*No relief*	*Totals*
Treated	10	50	60
Not treated	40	100	140
Totals	50	150	200

Use a suitable test to see if there is any association between treatment with the drug and relief of symptoms.

H_0: The treatment has no effect at all.
H_1: The treatment gives relief.

Table of expected values:

	Relief	*No relief*
Treated	$\frac{60 \times 50}{200} = 15$	$\frac{60 \times 150}{200} = 45$
Not treated	$\frac{140 \times 50}{200} = 35$	$\frac{140 \times 150}{200} = 105$

O	E	$\lvert O_i - E_i\rvert - \frac{1}{2}$	$\frac{(\lvert O_i - E_i\rvert - \frac{1}{2})^2}{E_i}$
10	15	4.5	1.35
50	45	4.5	0.45
40	35	4.5	0.578
100	105	4.5	0.193

$$\sum \frac{(\lvert O_i - E_i\rvert - \frac{1}{2})^2}{E_i} = 2.571$$

From Table 5 the critical value $\chi_1^2(5\%)$ is 3.841.

$$\sum \frac{(\lvert O_i - E_i\rvert - \frac{1}{2})^2}{E_i} < 3.841$$

So you do not reject H_0. There is no reason to believe there is an association between treatment and relief.

Exercise 5C

1 When analysing the results of a 3×2 contingency table it was found that

$$\sum_{i=1}^{6} \frac{(O_i - E_i)^2}{E_i} = 2.38$$

Write down the number of degrees of freedom and the critical value appropriate to these data in order to carry out a χ^2 test of significance at the 5% level. [L]

2 Three different types of locality were studied to see if the ownership, or non-ownership, of a television was or was not related to the locality. $\sum \frac{(O_i - E_i)^2}{E_i}$ was evaluated and found to be 13.1. Using a 5% level of significance, carry out a suitable test and state your conclusion.

3 In a college, three different groups of students sit the same examination. The results of the examination are classified as

Credit, Pass or Fail. In order to test whether or not there is a difference between the groups with respect to the proportions of students in the three grades, the statistic $\sum \frac{(O_i - E_i)^2}{E_i}$ is evaluated and found to be equal to 10.28.

(a) Explain why there are 4 degrees of freedom in this situation.

(b) Using a 5% level of significance, carry out the test and state your conclusions. [L]

4 The grades of 200 students in both Mathematics and English were studied with the following results.

		English grades		
		A	B	C
Maths grades	A	17	28	18
	B	38	45	16
	C	12	12	14

Using a 0.05 significance level, test to see if there is a relationship between English and Mathematics results. State your conclusions.

5 The number of trains on time, and the number of trains that were late was observed at three different London stations. The results were:

		Observed frequency	
		On time	*Late*
Station	A	26	14
	B	30	10
	C	44	26

Using the χ^2 statistic and a significance test at the 5% level, decide if there is any association between station and lateness.

6 In addition to being classed into grades A, B, C, D and E, 200 students are classified as male or female and their results summarised in a contingency table. Assuming all expected values are 5 or more, the statistic $\sum \frac{(O_i - E_i)^2}{E_i}$ was 14.27.

Stating your hypotheses and using a 1% significance level, investigate whether or not sex and grade are associated.

7 In a random sample of 60 articles made in factory A, 8 were defective. In factory B, 6 out of 40 similar articles were defective.

(a) Draw up a contingency table.

(b) Test at the 0.05 significance level the hypothesis that quality was independent of the factory involved.

8 During an influenza epidemic 15 boys and 8 girls became ill out of a class of 22 boys and 28 girls. Assuming that this class may be treated as a random sample of the age group, test the hypothesis that there is no connection between sex and susceptibility to influenza.

9 In a study of marine organisms a biologist collected specimens from three beaches and counted the number of males and females in each sample, with the following results:

		Beach		
		A	B	C
Sex	Male	46	80	40
	Female	54	120	160

Using a significance level of 5%, test if there is any difference between the beaches with regard to the numbers of male and female organisms.

10 A research worker studying the ages of adults and the number of credit cards they possess obtained the results shown below:

		Number of cards	
		$\leqslant 3$	> 3
Age	< 30	74	20
	$\geqslant 30$	50	35

Use the χ^2 statistic and a significance test at the 5% level to decide whether or not there is an association between age and number of credit cards possessed. [L]

SUMMARY OF KEY POINTS

1 $\sum \frac{(O_i - E_i)^2}{E_i} \sim \chi^2$

2 Degrees of freedom: $\nu =$ number of cells after combining − number of constraints.

3 If n is the number of cells after combining:

Distribution	*Degrees of freedom*	
	parameters known	*parameters not known*
Discrete uniform	$n-1$	
Binomial	$n-1$	$n-2$
Poisson	$n-1$	$n-2$
Normal	$n-1$	$n-3$ (both unknown) $n-2$ (one unknown)
Continuous uniform	$n-1$	

4 For contingency tables:

$$\text{Expected frequency} = \frac{\text{row total} \times \text{column total}}{\text{grand total}}$$

For an $h \times k$ table, degrees of freedom $\nu = (h-1)(k-1)$

5 Yates' correction for 2×2 tables:

$$\sum \frac{(|O_i - E_i| - \frac{1}{2})^2}{E_i} \sim \chi_1^2$$

Projects

6

Statistics is a practical subject. You have studied in Book T1 and this book a number of statistical techniques, but in general each one has been dealt with independently. A statistics project gives you the opportunity to show that you can apply a range of relevant techniques to the same problem in an appropriate manner.

A project should be on a subject of your own choice. It is vital that you think it through beforehand and draw up a strategy for achieving your aims.

6.1 Choosing a topic

This is perhaps the most difficult part of a project and the most important. A poor choice of topic can restrict your ability to demonstrate your statistical skills. Generally a project is most successful if you select a topic that interests you. The following areas can be considered.

Your hobbies and interests For example, suppose hockey is of great interest to you; you could choose to investigate the different ways of holding a hockey stick and their effect upon range and accuracy.

Other subjects you are studying These often pose statistical questions. A popular example of this is the biological study of limpets – what effect does the position on the beach have on limpet population and limpet size?

Your local environment and local interests For example, has your town or city recently had a bypass built? What effect has this had upon traffic volumes, traffic speeds, accident rates, etc.?

Current affairs Interest rates may be rising and you may be keen to know whether this has any effect upon unemployment, consumer spending, etc. This may tie in with work you are doing in economics.

Some further examples of project topics are given in section 6.9.

6.2 Formulating the hypotheses

When you have chosen your topic you may need to find out more about it by reading or talking to experts. This should prompt you to begin asking questions. For example, if you are from a rural area and dairy farming is one of your great interests you may pose one or more questions such as:

(a) Does the milk yield of a pedigree cow differ from that of a non-pedigree cow?

(b) Do the milk yields of a sample of cows follow a particular distribution?

(c) Is there a correlation between the number of weeks into lactation and the milk yields of cows?

Each of these can be formed into hypotheses that can then be investigated.

(a) H_0: There is no difference in the mean milk yields of pedigree and non-pedigree cows.
H_1: There is a difference in the mean milk yields of pedigree and non-pedigree cows.

(b) H_0: The milk yield follows a normal distribution. (When the graph is plotted you may decide another distribution would be a better model.)
H_1: The milk yield does not follow a normal distribution.

(c) H_0: There is no correlation between the length of lactation period and the milk yield of cows.

H_1: There is a correlation between lactation period and milk yield of cows.

There are many such questions that could have been posed, but these three were chosen because they involve different parts of the syllabus. They would form the basis for a good project that gives the opportunity to demonstrate a wide range of statistical skills.

6.3 Collecting and recording data

Having formed hypotheses you can now decide what your target population is going to be, the data you need to collect, and whether it is possible for you to collect it in the time at your disposal. If it is going to be difficult or too time consuming you should reconsider your choice of topic, or whether to reform your hypotheses to suit the data you *can* collect. When selecting your target population be as careful and concise as possible. For example, your population might be students in a particular college, or pebbles on a particular stretch of beach.

Data can be collected in many ways. Some possibilities are listed below:

(i) a designed experiment
(ii) direct observation and recording
(iii) simulation
(iv) questionnaires
(v) secondary sources.

In the case of the investigations into cows' milk yield, mentioned above, secondary data would be used. Most farmers keep extensive, often computerised, records of milk yields, and there are many publications giving digests of statistics that can be found in libraries. Other sources include CD-ROMs that may be accessed with a computer – your school may have this facility.

If you use primary data you must decide on how large a sample to take and how to collect it. In terms of sample size, 50 may give satisfactory results at the level at which you are working, although this should if possible be thought of as a minimum. You should also bear in mind that some assumptions can only be made if the sample is large. Do not be frightened to collect extra data if you think it necessary. Selection must be random in a statistical sense. Thought must be given to possible sources of bias and precautions that should be taken to avoid them. **Bias** is anything which occurs when taking a sample that prevents the sample from representing the population from which it is being taken. For example, sampling from an incomplete sampling frame, the introduction of personal subjective choice by the person taking the sample, responses that are only obtained from those who have a particular interest in the study, and the substitution of convenient sampling units when those that are required are not easily available, will all cause bias.

Recording your data needs to be carefully planned. It is worth thinking about how you will use your data and how much detail will be required. Drawing up a clear record sheet with adequate space for entering the various pieces of data will save you much time in the long run. If your data collection involves a questionnaire or interview, you should consider running a small pilot survey first so that any problems are sorted out and questions reworded if necessary. When designing questionnaires you should use simple language and keep questions as short as possible. You should ask only questions that are designed to produce simple answers, and not ask embarrassing questions, or ask questions outside the knowledge of the people being surveyed.

6.4 Analysing your data

Any analysis of data should be done to further the aims of the project. Diagrams, graphs and calculations should have a purpose: it is not necessary to display the data in every possible way. When producing diagrammatic representations of your data you should bear the following points in mind:

1. All diagrams should have titles and be properly labelled.
2. Charts that need to be compared should have the same scales. They should be on the same sheet of paper so comparisons can be made easily. Overlays can often be used to advantage.
3. Colour or shading can enhance diagrams.
4. Make sure the type of diagram used is suited to the type of data.

Always pick the most appropriate means of displaying data and the most relevant statistical calculations. A summary of some of the techniques you could use is given below.

Graphical representation

frequency tables
cumulative frequency polygons
line graphs
histograms
box and whisker plots
stem and leaf diagrams
scatter diagrams
contingency tables

Possible statistical models

discrete uniform
binomial
Poisson
normal
continuous uniform

Calculation and techniques

sample mean and variance
estimation of population mean and variance
distribution of sample means
confidence interval for sample means
central limit theorem
regression
correlation

Hypothesis tests

difference of means
mean of a normal
p of a binomial
mean of a Poisson
a correlation is zero
χ^2 goodness of fit
χ^2 contingency tables

Calculators and computers are excellent tools for the statistician, but if you are going to use either of these you must be sure you know what you are doing and explain each step you take in your report. Be selective in the statistics you calculate or use and do not let the computer dictate what you do.

6.5 Interpreting your results

Look at the results in relation to your original problem. Do they support your hypotheses or not? You should be aware that there may be factors at work other than those you have measured, and several equally feasible interpretations may be possible.

6.6 Conclusions

This is where you draw all the evidence together and consider how successful you were or were not in achieving your aims. If your results differ from those expected, you will need to suggest possible reasons for this. Any limitations or problems you encountered should also be discussed.

6.7 Writing up your report

The purpose of your report is to explain to the reader, in an easily understood manner, the work you have done, the reasons for doing it, the results that have been obtained and the conclusions that may be drawn. You will find it easy if you write up your report under the following headings:

(a) **Title**

(b) **Summary**: 100 to 200 words describing the main work undertaken and the conclusions reached. Although this should be placed at the front of your report it is the last thing you write.

(c) **Introduction**: a general statement of what you are going to do, the hypotheses you are going to test or the parameters to be estimated. A brief description of the strategies you hope to use.

(d) **Data collection**: Describe how you selected and collected your sample and your reasons for choosing the method you used. Include information on problems encountered, precautions taken and any checks made to ensure the data were suitable for the purpose. Any copies of questionnaires, experiment sheets, etc. should be put in an appendix at the end of the report.

(e) **Analysis of data**: Include all tables, diagrams, graphs and calculations.

(f) **Interpretation**: Discuss the ways in which the data, diagrams and calculations have furthered the aim of the project.

(g) **Conclusions**: Draw together all the evidence and state how well your aims have been achieved and what your results mean. If appropriate, suggest further work that could be carried out.

(h) **Appendices**: These may include a sample questionnaire, test papers, experiment sheets, lengthy calculations and any work not of direct relevance to the main report.

6.8 Project examples

It is not possible to give you examples of complete projects, but the outline plans of two are given. Each plan could be the basis of a good project but you should realise that if, for example, only one of the hypotheses is pursued, then you will restrict the range of techniques you can display. Marks will be low if you demonstrate only limited statistical skills.

PROJECT NUMBER ONE

TITLE: Milk yields of cows

HYPOTHESES:

(a) H_0: No difference between the milk yields of pedigree and non-pedigree cows.
(b) H_0: The milk yield of cows follows a normal distribution.
(c) H_0: there is no correlation between length of lactation and milk yields in cows.

DATA COLLECTION:

Secondary data from farm records. Milk yields of herds of pedigree and non-pedigree cows for one year.

GRAPHICAL REPRESENTATION:

Frequency tables
Box and whisker or bar chart for (a)
Histogram for (b)
Scatter diagram for (c)

SAMPLING STATISTICS:

Estimation of population mean and variance from sample
Correlation

POSSIBLE STATISTICAL MODEL:

Normal for (b)

HYPOTHESIS TESTS:

Difference of means for (a)
χ^2 goodness of fit for (b)
Testing a correlation is zero for (c)

INTERPRETATION AND CONCLUSIONS:

(a) Was there a difference in yield? If there is no difference why keep pedigree cows at all? Is yield the only important criterion in the production of milk? Are there other areas that could be investigated?

(b) Why should milk yield follow a normal distribution? Did it appear from your investigation that it did?
Are there any alternative distributions?

(c) How significant was the correlation found to be? What are the implications for milk production?

PROJECT NUMBER TWO

TITLE: Learning to drive

HYPOTHESES:

(a) H_0: Males and females take the same number of driving tests before they pass their test.

(b) H_0: There is no correlation between the day of the week a test is taken and the likelihood of passing.

(c) H_0: The number of hours of lessons taken by learner drivers before taking a driving test is normally distributed.

DATA COLLECTION:

By questionnaire to 100 randomly selected college students.

GRAPHICAL REPRESENTATION:

Frequency tables
Comparative bar chart for (a)
Contingency table for (b)
Histogram for (c)

SAMPLING STATISTICS:

Means for (a)
Estimation of population mean and variance for (c)

POSSIBLE STATISTICAL MODEL:

Normal

HYPOTHESIS TESTS:

Difference of means and normal distribution
χ^2 goodness of fit for both male and female pass rates for (a)
χ^2 contingency table for (b)
χ^2 goodness of fit for (c)

INTERPRETATION AND CONCLUSIONS:

(a) Do males and females take the same number of tests? If not, why is this so?

(b) Was the result for this hypothesis as you expected?

(c) Did the number of lessons required seem to follow a normal distribution? How much reliance can be put on the result?
Was the sample large enough?
Could any further work be done to improve the results?

6.9 Project topics

You should always try to think up your own topic for a project if possible, because original ideas often produce the best work. If you find this difficult, some of the ideas listed below might give you the inspiration to think up a project of your own. These topics require only easily accessible data. Through family connections you may have access to more unusual data – areas such as medicine, quality control, stock control and industrial experiment can often prove to be the starting point of a good project.

A few questions you might consider are given for the first twenty suggestions. You can probably think up others for yourself.

1 **Jelly babies** Are the colours uniformly distributed? In bags of the same weight do you get the same number of jelly babies? Do the weights of the bags follow a known distribution? Is there a difference between the colour preferences of males and females?

2 **Cars arriving at a petrol station** Does the rate at which cars arrive follow a particular distribution? Is there any difference between the number of arrivals on weekdays and at weekends? Does the type of petrol chosen by four-wheel drive off-road vehicles match that of ordinary cars?

3 **Memory** Is there a significant relationship between age and the ability to recall information? Is there any difference between visual and aural memory and is there any difference between the sexes in this respect?

4 **Height and shoe size** In a particular age group do these follow any known distribution? Is there any correlation between height and shoe size? (These types of questions could be applied to many pairs of variables, but you should always pick ones that you think are likely to be related in some way.)

5 **Prices of cars** Is there a relationship between the original price of a car and the rate at which it depreciates? Does the price of a new car depend upon its engine size? Does the frequency with which you see different colours of cars follow a uniform distribution? Is there a law relating engine size to petrol consumption?

6 **Pulse rates** What are the mean and expected variance of the pulse rates of a group of subjects? What would be the range of pulse rates within which we might expect 95% of the population to lie? Does pulse rate increase with exercise? Does pulse rate vary with age? Do pulse rates for a particular age group follow a particular distribution?

7 Tennis Does height affect speed of serve? How does the speed of serve compare in males and females? Is there any correlation between speed of service and ranking for top tennis players?

8 Literary style Is there a difference in the word length and sentence length of two different publications? For each publication is there any correlation between sentence length and the average word length in the sentence? What proportions of each publication are devoted to text and pictures? Are these proportions significantly different?

9 Unemployment and crime Does a rise in unemployment occur at the same time as a rise in crime? Is the relative unemployment rate of males and females the same today as it was ten years ago?

10 Examination results Is there any correlation between students' GCSE grades and their A-level grades? Do the grades for a particular subject follow a known distribution? Has there been a change in the proportions of A, B, C, etc. grades over the last ten years?

11 Pebbles on a beach Does the size of pebbles vary according to their location on the beach? Is there any correlation between the length and the breadth of pebbles? Do the sizes of pebbles at a particular site follow a normal distribution?

12 Left-handedness What proportion of a given sample of people are left-handed? What conclusions, if any, can be drawn about the whole population? Is there a significant difference between the proportion of left-handed males and the proportion of left-handed females? Is there an association between left-handedness and some other variable (e.g. wearing glasses, left-handed parent, etc.).

13 Birthdays What is the distribution of the frequency with which birthdays occur in each month? What is the estimate of the probability of birth on a given day? How does this differ from the theoretical value? What is the probability that in a given group of people 0, 1, 2, 3, etc., will have the same birthdays? Does this approximate to any particular distribution?

14 Doctor's surgery What distribution, if any, does the waiting time of patients follow? What is the probability of a patient having to wait, say, 20 minutes? Is there any difference between the numbers of men and women attending morning and evening surgeries?

15 Football Is there any correlation between goals scored and goals conceded by a set of teams over a season's matches? Does the rank position of a team bear any relationship to the goals scored? Do the numbers of goals scored on a particular day follow any known distribution?

16 Reading ability Do children who read well also do well in mathematics? Are there any differences in the scores for boys and the scores for girls? Do the scores follow a particular distribution?

17 Names Do people with long surnames give their children long first names? Are boys likely to be given longer names than girls? Do the lengths of names follow a particular distribution?

18 Fruit Is there a correlation between edible and non-edible proportions of a given sample of different fruit? Do the weights of the fruit follow a normal distribution?

19 Weeds What is the density of a particular weed in different environments? Is there any correlation between height and density? If the environments are ranked for dampness is there any correlation between density and dampness?

20 Pocket money Does the amount of pocket money received by young people vary with age? Is there any difference between the average pocket money for girls and that for boys for a particular age group? Is there any correlation between pocket money received and part-time earnings in a particular age group?

Other topics for investigation

With these topics you are left to form your own questions.

1. Germination of seeds
2. Accident rates
3. Trapping insects in both wet and sticky traps
4. Ambulance call outs
5. Shopping surveys
6. Days of absence from school for different age groups
7. Telephone calls in a school office
8. Part-time jobs
9. University entry grades, popularity of departments, etc.
10. Clothes
11. Peak expiratory flow rates
12. Advertising and sales
13. Road junctions – motorway traffic
14. Rainfall, temperature, sunshine, etc.
15. Rivers – speeds of flow, distance from source, etc.

16. Taste – distinguishing between two or more items such as margarine and butter
17. Television viewing
18. Extrasensory perception
19. General knowledge or other expertise
20. Consumer organisation information
21. Reaction times
22. Trains – lateness, satisfaction, etc.
23. Stock control
24. Quality control

Review exercise 2

1 The random variable Y has a χ^2 distribution with 10 degrees of freedom. Find y such that $\text{P}(Y < y) = 0.99$. [L]

2 Spearman's rank correlation coefficient between 7 pairs of ranks was calculated to be 0.79, based on $\sum d^2 = 12$. Stating your hypotheses and using a 5% level of significance, interpret the result. [L]

3 The random variable X has a chi-squared distribution with 8 degrees of freedom. Find x such that $\text{P}(X > x) = 0.05$.

4 As part of an investigation into visits to a Health Centre a 5×3 contingency table was constructed. A χ^2 test of significance at the 5% level is to be carried out on the table. Write down the number of degrees of freedom and the critical region appropriate to this test. [L]

5 A group of students scored the following marks in their Statistics and Geography examinations.

Student	A	B	C	D	E	F	G	H
Statistics	64	71	49	38	72	55	54	68
Geography	55	50	51	47	65	45	39	82

(a) Find the value of the Spearman rank correlation coefficient between the marks of these students.

(b) Stating your hypotheses and using a 5% level of significance, interpret your value. [L]

6 In an experiment the temperature of a metal rod was raised from 300 K. The extensions E mm of the rod at selected temperatures T K are shown in the table:

Extension of a metal rod

T	300	350	400	450	500	550	600	650	700
E	0	0.38	0.8	1.22	1.6	2	2.42	2.8	3.18

Draw a scatter diagram for these data and mark on your diagram the point representing the means of T and E.
Find the equation of the regression line of E on T and draw this line on your diagram.
Estimate the extension of the rod at 430 K. [L]

7 Data are collected in the form of a 4×4 contingency table. To carry out a χ^2 test of significance one of the rows was amalgamated with another row and the resulting value of $\sum \frac{(O-E)^2}{E}$ obtained.
Write down the number of degrees of freedom and the critical value of χ^2 appropriate to this test assuming a 5% significance level. [L]

8 The number of accidents per week at a certain road junction was monitored for four years. The results obtained are summarised in the table.

Number of accidents	0	1	2	>2
Number of weeks	112	56	40	0

Using a 5% level of significance, carry out a χ^2 test of the hypothesis that the number of accidents per week has a Poisson distribution. [L]

9 Six friesian cows were ranked in order of merit at an agricultural show by the official judge and by a student vet. The ranks were as follows:

Official judge	1	2	3	4	5	6
Student vet	1	5	4	2	6	3

(a) Calculate Spearman's rank correlation coefficient between these rankings.

(b) Investigate whether or not there was agreement between the rankings of the judge and the student.

State clearly your hypotheses, and carry out an appropriate one-tailed significance test at the 5% level. [L]

10 (a) Draw a diagram to illustrate the lengths whose sum of squares is minimised in the least squares method for finding the regression line of y on x.
State which is the independent and which is the dependent variable.

(b) The length (L mm) and width (W mm) of each of 20 individuals of species of fossil are measured. A summary of the results is:

$$\sum L = 400.20,\ \sum W = 176.00,\ \sum LW = 3700.20,$$
$$\sum L^2 = 8151.32,\ \sum W^2 = 1780.52$$

Obtain the product-moment correlation coefficient between the length and width of these fossils. Without performing a significance test interpret your results.

11 A manufacturer of batteries claims that his product has a mean life of 160 hours and that it is normally distributed with a standard deviation of 16 hours. To test this assertion 100 batteries were run until flat, with the following results:

Life (h)	120–	130–	140–	150–	160–	170–	180–	190–120
Frequency	11	9	14	14	17	15	10	10

Use a 5% significance level to test the manufacturer's claim.

12 Of the 14 fish of a particular species caught in lake A, 7 had a dark stripe. Of 20 fish of the same species caught in a second nearby lake B, 8 had a dark stripe. Assuming that each catch is a random sample of the fish in each lake, test the hypotheses that the fish in both lakes come from the same population. Use a 5% significance level.

13 Two schools enter their pupils for a particular public examination and the results obtained are shown below:

	Credit	*Pass*	*Fail*
School A	51	10	19
School B	39	10	21

By using an approximate χ^2 statistic, assess, at the 5% level, whether or not there is a significant difference between the two schools with respect to the number of passes in the three grades. State your null and alternative hypotheses. [L]

14 The following table is the result of analysing a random sample of the invoices submitted by branches of a large chain of bookshops.

	Novel	*Textbook*	*General interest*
Hardback	24	10	22
Paperback	66	10	18

By using an approximate χ^2 statistic, assess, at the 5% level, whether or not there is any association between the type of book sold and its cover.

State clearly your null and alternative hypotheses. [L]

15 A random sample of 100 housewives were asked whether or not they used brand X washing up liquid. 62 said yes and 38 said no. In a second random sample of 80 housewives, taken at a later date, 56 said yes and 24 said no. Draw up a 2×2 contingency table and use an appropriate test at the 5% level to see if the usage of brand X washing powder has altered.

16 A delivery of iron ore arrives at a factory in a large lorry. 40 random samples are taken from the ore with the following results:

% iron centre of interval	30	32	34	36
Frequency	8	13	12	7

(a) Estimate the mean % iron content of the ore in the lorry.

(b) Use a test at the 5% level of significance to see if the distribution of the iron content of the ore can be modelled by a normal distribution with $\sigma = 2.023$.

17 As part of a survey in a particular profession, age, x years, and salary, £y thousands, were recorded.
The values of x and y for a randomly selected sample of ten members of the profession are as follows:

x	30	52	38	48	56	44	41	25	32	27
y	22	38	40	34	35	32	28	27	29	41

(a) Calculate, to 3 decimal places, the product-moment correlation coefficient between age and salary.

(b) State two conditions under which it might be appropriate to use Spearman's rank correlation coefficient.

(c) Calculate, to 3 decimal places, the Spearman's rank correlation coefficient between age and salary.

It is suggested that there is no correlation between age and salary.

(d) Set up appropriate null and alternative hypotheses and carry out an appropriate test. [L]

18 A study was done of how many students in a college were left-handed and how many were right-handed. As well as left- or right-handedness the sex of each person was also recorded with the following results:

	Left-handed	*Right-handed*
Male	10	60
Female	8	80

Use a significance test at the 0.05 level to see if there is an association between sex and left and right handedness.

19 A machine hire company kept records of the age, X months, and the maintenance costs, £Y, of one type of machine. The following table summarises the data for a random sample of 10 machines.

Machine	A	B	C	D	E	F	G	H	I	J
Age, x	63	12	34	81	51	14	45	74	24	89
Maintenance costs, y	111	25	41	181	64	21	51	145	43	241

(a) Plot a scatter diagram of these data.

(b) Calculate, to 3 decimal places, the product-moment correlation coefficient. (You may use $\sum x^2 = 30\,625$, $\sum y^2 = 135\,481$, $\sum xy = 62\,412$)

(c) Calculate, to 3 decimal places, the Spearman's rank correlation coefficient.

(d) It is suggested that it would have been better to have calculated the coefficients above for X and $\ln Y$ instead of X and Y. Without doing any calculations, state any changes you would expect to find in the values of the coefficients.

(e) For a different type of machine similar data were collected. From a large population of such machines a random sample of 10 was taken and the Spearman rank correlation coefficient, based on $\sum d^2 = 36$, was 0.782. Using a 5% level of significance and quoting from the tables of critical values, interpret this rank correlation coefficient. Use a two-tailed test and state clearly your null and alternative hypotheses. [L]

20 Successful contestants in a TV game show were allowed to select from one of five boxes, four of which contained prizes, and one of which contained nothing. The boxes were numbered 1 to 5, and, when the show had run for 100 weeks, the choices made by the contestants were analysed with the following results:

Box number	1	2	3	4	5
Frequency	20	16	25	18	21

(a) Explain why these data could possibly be modelled by a discrete uniform distribution.

(b) Using a significance level of 5%, test to see if the discrete uniform distribution is a good model in this particular case.

21 Over a period of time a garage records the number of second-hand cars sold per week (y), and the amount spent on advertising in the local paper (x). The table shows the data collected for 10 weeks picked at random from one year's figures.

Week	A	B	C	D	E	F	G	H	I	J
Expenditure (£x)	360	250	410	560	200	680	710	350	400	430
Cars sold (y)	13	12	17	20	9	21	23	12	17	16

(a) Find S_{xy} and S_{xx}.

(b) Find the equation of the regression line.

(c) Give an interpretation of the coefficients in your equation.

(d) Estimate the number of cars likely to be sold if £300 is spent on advertising.

22 A pesticide was tested by applying it in the form of a spray to 50 samples of 5 flies. The numbers of dead flies after 1 hour were then counted with the following results:

Number of dead flies	0	1	2	3	4	5
Frequency	1	1	5	11	24	8

(a) Calculate the probability that a fly dies when sprayed.

(b) Using a significance level of 5%, test to see if these data could be modelled by a binomial distribution.

23 In a wine-growing region, 6 consecutive years were ranked for sunshine, the year with most sunshine being given the rank 1. For each of these years, the yield of grapes (tonnes) was also recorded. The results are shown in the table on the next page.

Yield of grapes and rank of the amount of sunshine

Year	1	2	3	4	5	6
Yield (tonnes)	76	52	73	61	59	78
Sunshine (rank)	1	5	4	3	6	2

Using a 5% significance level, investigate whether or not these data indicate a positive correlation between the rankings of sunshine and grape yield. (You must make a clear statement of your null hypothesis.) [L]

24 A small shop sells a particular item at a fairly steady yearly rate. When looking at the weekly sales it was found that the number sold varied. The results for the 50 weeks the shop was open were as shown in the table.

Weekly sales	0	1	2	3	4	5	6	7	8	>8
Frequency	0	4	7	8	10	6	7	4	4	0

(a) Find the mean number of sales per week.

(b) Using a significance level of 5%, test to see if these can be modelled by a Poisson distribution.

25 Explain briefly, referring to your project work if you wish, the conditions under which you would measure association by using a rank correlation coefficient rather than a product-moment coefficient.

At an agricultural show 10 Shetland sheep were ranked by a qualified judge and by a trainee judge. Their rankings are shown in the table.

Qualified judge	1	2	3	4	5	6	7	8	9	10
Trainee judge	1	2	5	6	7	8	10	4	3	9

Calculate a rank correlation coefficient for these data.

Using a suitable table and a 5% significance level, state your conclusions as to whether there is some degree of agreement between the two sets of ranks. [L]

26 Samples of stones were taken at two points on a beach which were 1 mile apart. The rock types of the stones were found and classified as igneous, sedimentary or other types, with the following results.

		Site	
		A	*B*
Rock type	*Igneous*	30	10
	Sedimentary	55	35
	Other	15	15

Use a 5% significance level to see if the rocks at both sites come from the same population.

27 Components which are produced by a certain machine are deposited into plastic bins as they are produced. It is thought that the machine will produce only 5% defective components. Samples of 20 components are taken from each of the bins with the following results:

Number of defects	0	1	2	3	4	5
Frequency	20	31	30	10	6	3

(a) Use a significance level of 5% and an appropriate test to see if these results can be modelled by a binomial distribution with $p = 0.05$.

(b) Estimate a value for p from your data and using this value repeat the above test.

28 A company monitored the number of days (x) of business trips taken by executives of the company and the corresponding claims (£y) they submitted to cover the total expenditure of these trips.
A random sample of 10 trips gave the following results.

x (days)	10	3	8	17	5	9	14	16	21	13
y (£)	116	39	85	159	61	94	143	178	225	134

(a) Plot these data on a scatter diagram.

Give a reason to support the calculation of a regression line through these points.

(b) Find an equation of the regression line of y on x, in the form $y = a + bx$.

(c) Interpret the slope b and intercept a of your line.

(d) Find the expected expenditure of a trip lasting 11 days.

(e) State, giving a reason, whether or not you would use the line to find the expected expenditure of a trip lasting 2 months. [L]

29 The table below shows the number of employees and the number of accidents they had during one year for each of four factories.

Factory	A	B	C	D
Employees (thousands)	3	5	2	1
Accidents	15	30	18	12

Test (at the 5% level of significance) the hypothesis that the accident rate is the same for all factories.

30 A teacher recorded the following data which refer to the marks gained by 13 children in an aptitude test and a statistics examination.

Child	A	B	C	D	E	F	G	H	I	J	K	L	M
Aptitude test (x)	54	52	42	31	43	23	32	49	37	13	13	36	39
Statistics examination (y)	84	68	71	37	79	58	33	60	47	60	44	64	49

(a) Draw a scatter diagram to represent these two sets of marks.

(b) Calculate, to 3 decimal places, the product-moment correlation coefficient between the test mark and the examination mark.

(c) Comment on your result.

(d) The teacher decides on the basis of the diagram that children F, J and K performed differently to the rest of the group, and decides to analyse the data ignoring these three children. Calculate, to 3 decimal places, the Spearman rank correlation coefficient between the other 10 pairs of observations.

(e) Using a 5% significance level and quoting from the table of critical values interpret the rank correlation coefficient (use a one-tailed test). State clearly your null and alternative hypotheses. [L]

31 (a) Explain briefly, without doing any algebra, the method by which the principle of least squares can be used to find the equation of a regression line. Show on a sketch the distances whose sum of squares is minimised, and mark clearly which axis records the dependent variable and which the independent variable.

The consumption, in millions of gallons of beer, in a certain country for the years 1976 to 1983 is shown:

Year	1976	1977	1978	1979	1980	1981	1982	1983
Consumption	31	33.7	33.8	35.2	39.3	43.3	42.6	45.1

(b) Draw a scatter diagram to represent these data.

(c) Find the equation of the regression line of consumption on year, giving the slope to 2 decimal places, and the intercept to the nearest integer. Draw this line on your diagram.

(d) Use your equation to estimate the consumption for 1984. In making this estimate, state any assumptions which you are making. [L]

32 A tensile test is carried out on 100 steel bars which are uniform in section. The distances from the mid-points of the bars at which they fracture is recorded with the following results.

Distance (cm)	0–10	–20	–30	–40	–50	–60
Frequency	15	17	18	20	12	18

Test at the 0.05 significance level if these data can be modelled by a continuous uniform distribution.

33 For 12 consecutive months a factory manager recorded the number of items produced by the factory and the total cost of their production. The following table summarises the manager's data.

Number of items, x (thousands)	18	36	45	22	69	72	13	33	59	79	10	53
Production cost, y (£1000)	37	54	63	42	84	91	33	49	79	98	32	71

(a) Draw a scatter diagram for the data.

(b) Give a reason to support the use of a regression line $y = a + bx$ as a suitable model for these data.

(c) Obtain the regression equation for y on x for these data, giving a to 3 significant figures.

(d) Give a practical interpretation for a and b.

(e) The selling price of each item produced is £1.60. Find the level of output at which total income and estimated total costs are equal. Give a brief interpretation of this value.

34 Within a certain tribe it was found that 15% had blood which was rhesus negative. A study done at a later date took samples of 10 people from different areas within the tribe's boundary, and found how many had rhesus negative blood in each of the samples, with the following results.

Number of rhesus negative	0	1	2	3	>3
Frequency	23	30	32	10	5

Use a suitable test with a 5% significance level to see if these are consistent with a binomial distribution with $p = 0.15$.

35 An expert on porcelain is asked to place seven china bowls in date order of manufacture, assigning the rank 1 to the oldest bowl. The actual dates of manufacture and the order given by the expert are shown below.

Bowl	A	B	C	D	E	F	G
Date of manufacture	1920	1857	1710	1896	1810	1690	1780
Order given by expert	7	3	4	6	2	1	5

(a) Find, to 3 decimal places, the Spearman rank correlation coefficient between the order of manufacture and the order given by the expert.

(b) Refer to the table of critical values to comment on your results. State clearly the null hypothesis being tested. [L]

36 A manufactured article is made on four similar machines. The numbers of defective items found in random samples taken from the output of the machines are shown below.

Machine	A	B	C	D
Number of defective articles	10	3	5	8
Number of non-defective articles	150	77	95	62

Is there evidence, at the 5% significance level, to suggest that the defect rate is not the same for all machines?

37 Explain briefly what is measured by a correlation coefficient. It is usual to expect that the total number of hours studied (x) in preparation for an examination would have a direct association with the number of marks attained (y) in that examination. The results below are for a sample of 10 students selected at random from a large class.

Hours studied (x)	6	15	7	17	19	3	13	11	10	17
Examination marks (y)	36	67	44	85	89	26	50	63	51	80

(a) Draw a scatter diagram to represent these data.

(b) Calculate, to 2 decimal places, the product-moment correlation coefficient between x and y.

(c) Without performing a significance test, interpret your result.

(d) Explain how the scatter diagram supports your result in (b).

38 The data below show the height above sea level, x metres, and the temperature, y °C, at 7.00 a.m., on the same day in summer at nine places in Europe.

Height, x (m)	1400	400	280	790	390	590	540	1250	680
Temperature, y (°C)	6	15	18	10	16	14	13	7	13

(a) Plot these data on a scatter diagram.

(b) Calculate the product-moment correlation coefficient between x and y.

(c) Give an interpretation of your coefficient.

On the same day the number of hours of sunshine was recorded and Spearman's rank correlation between hours of sunshine and temperature, based on $\sum d^2 = 28$, was 0.767.

(d) Stating your hypotheses and using a 5% two-tailed test, interpret this rank correlation coefficient. [L]

39 An experiment was conducted to determine the value of a variable y when another variable x had values $x_1, x_2, \ldots, x_n$. Denoting the observed values of y by $y_1, y_2, \ldots, y_n$, the pairs of values $(x_1, y_1), (x_2, y_2), \ldots (x_n, y_n)$ are plotted on a graph. Describe the method of least squares for fitting a straight line to the plotted points, making a clear statement of the quantity which is minimised by this method.

A large field of maize was divided into six plots of equal area and each plot fertilised with a different concentration of fertiliser. The yield of maize from each plot is shown below.

Concentration (*oz* m^{-2})	0	1	2	3	4	5
Yield (*tonnes*)	15	22	31	40	48	54

(a) Draw a scatter diagram for these data.

(b) Obtain the equation of the regression line for yield on concentration, giving the values of the coefficients to 2 decimal places.

(c) Use the regression line to obtain a value for the yield when the concentration is $3\,\text{oz}\,\text{m}^{-2}$. State precisely what is being estimated by this value.

(d) State any reservations you would have about making an estimate from the regression equation of the expected yield per plot if 7 oz m^{-2} of fertiliser are applied. [L]

40 During an experiment 150 people were asked to choose a number between 1 and 9 with the following results.

Number	1	2	3	4	5	6	7	8	9
Frequency	6	20	28	15	14	20	27	13	7

Using a significance level of 0.05, test the hypothesis that people chose their number at random.

41 In a ski-jump contest each competitor made two jumps. The order of merit for the 10 competitors who completed both jumps are shown.

Ski-jumper	A	B	C	D	E	F	G	H	I	J
First jump	2	9	7	4	10	8	6	5	1	3
Second jump	4	10	5	1	8	9	2	7	3	6

(a) Calculate, to 2 decimal places, a rank correlation coefficient for the performance of the ski-jumpers in the two jumps.

(b) Using a 5% significance, and quoting from the table of critical values, interpret your result. State your null and alternative hypotheses clearly. [L]

42 A factory produces a serum for use in hospitals. The number of bacteria per 1 ml of serum is thought to have a Poisson distribution with a mean of 3. The laboratory producing the serum tested 150 batches with the following results.

Number of bacteria	0	1	2	3	4	5	6	7	8
Frequency	10	18	27	38	28	14	10	5	0

Test at the 5% significance level, to see if the assumption is correct.

43 (a) Explain briefly the conditions under which you would measure association using a rank correlation coefficient.

(b) Nine applicants for places at a college were interviewed by two tutors. Each tutor ranked the applicants in order of merit. The rankings are shown below.

Applicant	A	B	C	D	E	F	G	H	I
Tutor 1	1	2	3	4	5	6	7	8	9
Tutor 2	1	3	5	4	2	7	9	8	6

Use the table provided to investigate the extent of the agreement between the two tutors. [L]

44 The management of a factory buy a new machine which, it is claimed, produces on average 4 defective items during a normal working day. After installation the number of defective items produced each day over 100 consecutive days was as follows.

Number of defective items per day	0	1	2	3	4	5	6	7	8
Frequency	2	5	8	23	24	19	13	6	0

(a) Suggest reasons why these data might be modelled by a Poisson distribution with $\lambda = 4$.

(b) Using a 5% level of significance, carry out a test to see if a Poisson with $\lambda = 4$ is or is not a good model.

45 (a) Two judges at a cat show place the 10 entries in the following rank orders.

Cat	A	B	C	D	E	F	G	H	I	J
First judge	4	6	1	2	5	3	10	9	8	7
Second judge	2	9	3	1	7	4	6	8	5	10

Find a coefficient of rank correlation between the two rankings and, using the tables provided, comment on the extent of the agreement between the two judges.

(b) Explain briefly the role of the null and alternative hypotheses in a test of significance. [L]

46 Bottles of mineral water are delivered to shops in crates of 12 bottles. The weights of the bottles in 12 such crates were investigated with the following results.

Weight (kg)	2.1–	2.3–	2.5–	2.7–	2.9–	3.1–3.3
Frequency	11	19	43	35	22	14

(a) Using a significance level of 0.05, test to see if a normal distribution would be a good model for these data. (You may use mean weight $= 2.7$ and $s = 0.274$. These values have been calculated from these data.)

(b) Treating these as a random sample of all bottles produced that week, estimate how many had a weight below 2.2 kg if there were 2000 crates produced all told.

47 (a) Explain briefly the use of a null hypothesis and a level of significance in statistical work.

(b) The positions in a league table of 8 rugby clubs at the end of a season are shown, together with the average attendance (in hundreds) at home matches during the season.

Club	A	B	C	D	E	F	G	H
Position	1	2	3	4	5	6	7	8
Average attendance	30	32	12	19	27	18	15	25

Calculate the coefficient of rank correlation between position in the league and home attendance. Comment on your results. [L]

48 100 bolts were tested for tensile strength with the following results.

Tensile strength $(kg\,m^{-2})$	405–415	–425	–435	–445	–455	–465
Frequency	14	11	21	34	12	8

Using a significance level of 5%, test to see if a normal distribution would be a good model for these data.

49 The ages, in months, and the weights, in kg, of a random sample of nine babies are shown in the table overleaf.

Baby	A	B	C	D	E	F	G	H	I
Age (x)	1	2	2	3	3	3	4	4	5
Weight (y)	4.4	5.2	5.8	6.4	6.7	7.2	7.6	7.9	8.4

(a) Calculate, to 3 decimal places, the product-moment correlation coefficient between weight and age for these babies. Give a brief interpretation of your results.

(b) A boy who does not know the weights or ages of these babies is asked to list them, by guesswork, in order of increasing weight. He puts them in the order

A C E B G D I F H

Obtain, to 3 decimal places, a rank correlation coefficient between the boy's order and the true weight order.

(c) Referring to the tables and using a 5% significance level, discuss any conclusions you draw from your results. [L]

50 (a) State the quantity that is minimised when using the method of least squares. Use a sketch to illustrate your answer.

The heat output of wood is known to vary with the percentage moisture content. The table below shows, in suitable units, the data obtained from an experiment carried out to assess this variation.

Percentage moisture content (x)	50	8	34	22	45	15	74	82	60	30
Heat output (y)	5.5	7.4	6.2	6.8	5.5	7.1	4.4	3.9	4.9	6.3

(b) Obtain the equation of the regression line for heat output on percentage moisture content, giving the values of the coefficients to 2 decimal places.

(c) Use your equation to estimate the heat output of wood with 40% moisture content. State any reservations you would have about making an estimate from the regression equation of the heat output for a 90% moisture content.

(d) Explain briefly the main implication of your analysis for a person wishing to use wood as a form of heating. [L]

Examination style paper T2

Attempt all questions **Time 90 minutes**

1. The weight of Scrummy chocolate bars is normally distributed with a mean of 120 g and standard deviation 5 g.
Find the probability that the mean weight of a random sample of 16 such chocolate bars exceeds 122 g. [L]

(4 marks)

2. A class of primary school children consists of 16 boys and 16 girls. Each day 8 of the children are brought to school by car and the others walk. The teacher wishes to estimate the average distance travelled to school each day by the pupils in the class and decides to take a sample of size 12.

(*a*) Suggest a suitable method of sampling.

(*b*) Using the table of random numbers by rows and starting with the first row of numbers 86, 13, 84, 10 . . . describe how the teacher should take the sample.

(7 marks)

3. A machine is known to dispense liquid into cartons such that the volume dispensed is normally distributed with a standard deviation of 3.4 ml. It is claimed by the manufacturer of the machine that the mean volume dispensed is 100 ml.
In a series of trials on the machine the following values were recorded.

104.4	101.7	103.6	99.2	102.2
107.6	96.2	105.8	104.7	98.6

(*a*) Find a 95% symmetrical confidence interval for the mean volume of liquid dispensed by the machine.

(b) Use your interval to comment on the claim of the manufacturer.
Comment on the likely reaction of customers receiving cartons from the machine.
(c) Estimate how many samples should be taken if the probability that the sample mean is within 1.5 ml of the true value is 0.95. [L]

(12 marks)

4. A survey of the number of hours spent watching television each week was carried out. The sample, randomly selected from a large population, contained 240 males and 200 females. The results are summarised below.

	Male	Female
Under 10 hours	40.0%	32.5%
10–25	47.5%	51.5%
Over 25 hours	12.5%	16.0%

Use an approximate χ^2 statistic at the 5% level of significance to assess whether or not there is any association between gender and time spent watching television. [L]

(14 marks)

5. A group of children sat a Mathematics test and a Verbal Reasoning test. Their results are as follows, where x represents their Mathematics score and y their Verbal Reasoning score.

x	21	4	12	15	11	13	17	29	15	15
y	39	30	22	28	25	37	20	45	32	34

(*a*) Calculate the value of the product-moment correlation coefficient, r, between x and y.
(You may use $\sum x^2 = 2696$, $\sum y^2 = 10\,288$, $\sum xy = 5014$)
(*b*) Stating your hypotheses clearly test, at the 5% level, whether or not the correlation coefficient is significantly greater than zero.

A school uses both of these tests to assess new pupils when they join. A parent governor has suggested that asking the pupils to do two tests is too much and the school should consider using just one test. In response to this suggestion the headteacher said that the school would like to keep both tests as they measure different abilities.

(*c*) Assess the headteacher's comment in the light of the calculations in parts (*a*) and (*b*).

(14 marks)

6. Over a period of time a publishing house records the sales, y thousand, of 10 similar textbooks, and the amount, £x hundred, spent on advertising each book. The following table shows the data for the 10 books.

x	0.75	3.90	1.65	1.60	4.40	3.05	3.55	2.65	0.45	2.00
y	2.00	5.35	3.00	2.40	5.95	4.50	4.60	3.65	1.30	3.25

(*a*) Find the equation of the regression line of y on x, giving the coefficients to 2 decimal places.
(You may use $\sum x^2 = 73.5450$; $\sum y^2 = 149.7700$;
$\sum xy = 104.1475$)

(*b*) Give an interpretation of the coefficients in your equation.

(*c*) Estimate the number of textbooks sold if the publisher spends £375 on advertising.

For a set of novels, the publisher found the sales and advertising to be related by the equation

$$(y - 3.6) = 0.25(x - 2.4).$$

(*d*) Re-write the equation of the regression line in (*a*) in the form $(y - \bar{y}) = m(x - \bar{x})$ and compare the effect of advertising on the sales of textbooks and novels. [L]

(15 marks)

7. Emissions from a radioactive source occur at random with rate λ per minute. To test the null hypothesis H_0: $\lambda = 2$ against the alternative hypothesis H_1: $\lambda > 2$, the number, X, of emissions that occur in a randomly selected one minute interval is counted.

Three possible forms of the critical region for use in testing hypotheses are (i) $X \leqslant c$, (ii) $X \geqslant c$ and (iii) $X \leqslant c_1$ or $X \geqslant c_2$.

(*a*) State, giving a reason, which is the appropriate one to use in this case.

(*b*) Derive the critical region so that P(type I error) is as close to 0.05 as possible.

(*c*) State P(type I error) in this case.

(*d*) Find the probability of a type II error associated with the test you have obtained, for the case $\lambda = 4$.

(*e*) In a randomly chosen one minute interval, there were 4 emissions.

What conclusion can you draw?

(15 marks)

8. A biologist is trying to model the number of female kittens born in a litter. She has examined 250 litters of size 5 and obtained the following results.

Number of females	0	1	2	3	4	5
Number of litters	2	40	90	85	30	3

(*a*) Test at the 5% level of significance whether or not the binomial distribution with parameters $n = 5$ and $p = 0.5$ is an adequate model for these data.

The biologist decides to refine the model and uses the above data to estimate the proportion p of kittens that are female.

(*b*) Find this estimate of p.

Using this value of p she went on to calculate expected frequencies and the statistic $\sum \frac{(O - E)^2}{E}$ and obtained the value 10.951 (no classes were combined).

(*c*) Stating your hypotheses clearly, explain what conclusions the biologist should deduce from this value. Use a 5% level of significance.

(*d*) What are the implications of this analysis for the number of female kittens in a litter of 5?

(19 marks)

Appendix

Table 1 Binomial cumulative distribution function

The tabulated value is $P(X \leqslant x)$, where X has a binomial distribution with index x and parameter p.

$p =$	0.05	0.10	0.15	0.20	0.25	0.30	0.35	0.40	0.45	0.50
$n = 5, x = 0$	0.7738	0.5905	0.4437	0.3277	0.2373	0.1681	0.1160	0.0778	0.0503	0.0312
1	0.9774	0.9185	0.8352	0.7373	0.6328	0.5282	0.4284	0.3370	0.2562	0.1875
2	0.9988	0.9914	0.9734	0.9421	0.8965	0.8369	0.7648	0.6826	0.5931	0.5000
3	1.0000	0.9995	0.9978	0.9933	0.9844	0.9692	0.9460	0.9130	0.8688	0.8125
4	1.0000	1.0000	0.9999	0.9997	0.9990	0.9976	0.9947	0.9898	0.9815	0.9688
$n = 10, x = 0$	0.5987	0.3487	0.1969	0.1074	0.0563	0.0282	0.0135	0.0060	0.0025	0.0010
1	0.9139	0.7361	0.5443	0.3758	0.2440	0.1493	0.0860	0.0464	0.0233	0.0107
2	0.9885	0.9298	0.8202	0.6778	0.5256	0.3828	0.2616	0.1673	0.0996	0.0547
3	0.9990	0.9872	0.9500	0.8791	0.7759	0.6496	0.5138	0.3823	0.2660	0.1719
4	0.9999	0.9984	0.9901	0.9672	0.9219	0.8497	0.7515	0.6331	0.5044	0.3770
5	1.0000	0.9999	0.9986	0.9936	0.9803	0.9527	0.9051	0.8338	0.7384	0.6230
6	1.0000	1.0000	0.9999	0.9991	0.9965	0.9894	0.9740	0.9452	0.8980	0.8281
7	1.0000	1.0000	1.0000	0.9999	0.9996	0.9984	0.9952	0.9877	0.9726	0.9453
8	1.0000	1.0000	1.0000	1.0000	1.0000	0.9999	0.9995	0.9983	0.9955	0.9893
9	1.0000	1.0000	1.0000	1.0000	1.0000	1.0000	1.0000	0.9999	0.9997	0.9990
$n = 20, x = 0$	0.3585	0.1216	0.0388	0.0115	0.0032	0.0008	0.0002	0.0000	0.0000	0.0000
1	0.7358	0.3917	0.1756	0.0692	0.0243	0.0076	0.0021	0.0005	0.0001	0.0000
2	0.9245	0.6769	0.4049	0.2061	0.0913	0.0355	0.0121	0.0036	0.0009	0.0002
3	0.9841	0.8670	0.6477	0.4114	0.2252	0.1071	0.0444	0.0160	0.0049	0.0013
4	0.9974	0.9568	0.8298	0.6296	0.4148	0.2375	0.1182	0.0510	0.0189	0.0059
5	0.9997	0.9887	0.9327	0.8042	0.6172	0.4164	0.2454	0.1256	0.0553	0.0207
6	1.0000	0.9976	0.9781	0.9133	0.7858	0.6080	0.4166	0.2500	0.1299	0.0577
7	1.0000	0.9996	0.9941	0.9679	0.8982	0.7723	0.6010	0.4159	0.2520	0.1316
8	1.0000	0.9999	0.9987	0.9900	0.9591	0.8867	0.7624	0.5956	0.4143	0.2517
9	1.0000	1.0000	0.9998	0.9974	0.9861	0.9520	0.8782	0.7553	0.5914	0.4119
10	1.0000	1.0000	1.0000	0.9994	0.9961	0.9829	0.9468	0.8725	0.7507	0.5881
11	1.0000	1.0000	1.0000	0.9999	0.9991	0.9949	0.9804	0.9435	0.8692	0.7483
12	1.0000	1.0000	1.0000	1.0000	0.9998	0.9987	0.9940	0.9790	0.9420	0.8684
13	1.0000	1.0000	1.0000	1.0000	1.0000	0.9997	0.9985	0.9935	0.9786	0.9423
14	1.0000	1.0000	1.0000	1.0000	1.0000	1.0000	0.9997	0.9984	0.9936	0.9793
15	1.0000	1.0000	1.0000	1.0000	1.0000	1.0000	1.0000	0.9997	0.9985	0.9941
16	1.0000	1.0000	1.0000	1.0000	1.0000	1.0000	1.0000	1.0000	0.9997	0.9987
17	1.0000	1.0000	1.0000	1.0000	1.0000	1.0000	1.0000	1.0000	1.0000	0.9998
18	1.0000	1.0000	1.0000	1.0000	1.0000	1.0000	1.0000	1.0000	1.0000	1.0000

Table 2 Poisson cumulative distribution function

The tabulated value is $P(X \leqslant x)$, where X has a Poisson distribution with parameter μ.

$\mu =$	0.5	1.0	1.5	2.0	2.5	3.0	3.5	4.0	4.5	5.0
$x = 0$	0.6065	0.3679	0.2231	0.1353	0.0821	0.0498	0.0302	0.0183	0.0111	0.0067
1	0.9098	0.7358	0.5578	0.4060	0.2873	0.1991	0.1359	0.0916	0.0611	0.0404
2	0.9856	0.9197	0.8088	0.6767	0.5438	0.4232	0.3208	0.2381	0.1736	0.1247
3	0.9982	0.9810	0.9344	0.8571	0.7576	0.6472	0.5366	0.4335	0.3423	0.2650
4	0.9998	0.9963	0.9814	0.9473	0.8912	0.8153	0.7254	0.6288	0.5321	0.4405
5	1.0000	0.9994	0.9955	0.9834	0.9580	0.9161	0.8576	0.7851	0.7029	0.6160
6	1.0000	0.9999	0.9991	0.9955	0.9858	0.9665	0.9347	0.8893	0.8311	0.7622
7	1.0000	1.0000	0.9998	0.9989	0.9958	0.9881	0.9733	0.9489	0.9134	0.8666
8	1.0000	1.0000	1.0000	0.9998	0.9989	0.9962	0.9901	0.9786	0.9597	0.9319
9	1.0000	1.0000	1.0000	1.0000	0.9997	0.9989	0.9967	0.9919	0.9829	0.9682
10	1.0000	1.0000	1.0000	1.0000	0.9999	0.9997	0.9990	0.9972	0.9933	0.9863
11	1.0000	1.0000	1.0000	1.0000	1.0000	0.9999	0.9997	0.9991	0.9976	0.9945
12	1.0000	1.0000	1.0000	1.0000	1.0000	1.0000	0.9999	0.9997	0.9992	0.9980
13	1.0000	1.0000	1.0000	1.0000	1.0000	1.0000	1.0000	0.9999	0.9997	0.9993
14	1.0000	1.0000	1.0000	1.0000	1.0000	1.0000	1.0000	1.0000	0.9999	0.9998
15	1.0000	1.0000	1.0000	1.0000	1.0000	1.0000	1.0000	1.0000	1.0000	0.9999
16	1.0000	1.0000	1.0000	1.0000	1.0000	1.0000	1.0000	1.0000	1.0000	1.0000
17	1.0000	1.0000	1.0000	1.0000	1.0000	1.0000	1.0000	1.0000	1.0000	1.0000
18	1.0000	1.0000	1.0000	1.0000	1.0000	1.0000	1.0000	1.0000	1.0000	1.0000
19	1.0000	1.0000	1.0000	1.0000	1.0000	1.0000	1.0000	1.0000	1.0000	1.0000

$u =$	5.5	6.0	6.5	7.0	7.5	8.0	8.5	9.0	9.5	10.0
$x = 0$	0.0041	0.0025	0.0015	0.0009	0.0006	0.0003	0.0002	0.0001	0.0001	0.0000
1	0.0266	0.0174	0.0113	0.0073	0.0047	0.0030	0.0019	0.0012	0.0008	0.0005
2	0.0884	0.0620	0.0430	0.0296	0.0203	0.0138	0.0093	0.0062	0.0042	0.0028
3	0.2017	0.1512	0.1118	0.0818	0.0591	0.0424	0.0301	0.0212	0.0149	0.0103
4	0.3575	0.2851	0.2237	0.1730	0.1321	0.0996	0.0744	0.0550	0.0403	0.0293
5	0.5289	0.4457	0.3690	0.3007	0.2414	0.1912	0.1496	0.1157	0.0885	0.0671
6	0.6860	0.6063	0.5265	0.4497	0.3782	0.3134	0.2562	0.2068	0.1649	0.1301
7	0.8095	0.7440	0.6728	0.5987	0.5246	0.4530	0.3856	0.3239	0.2687	0.2202
8	0.8944	0.8472	0.7916	0.7291	0.6620	0.5925	0.5231	0.4557	0.3918	0.3328
9	0.9462	0.9161	0.8774	0.8305	0.7764	0.7166	0.6530	0.5874	0.5218	0.4579
10	0.9747	0.9574	0.9332	0.9015	0.8622	0.8159	0.7634	0.7060	0.6453	0.5830
11	0.9890	0.9799	0.9661	0.9467	0.9208	0.8881	0.8487	0.8030	0.7520	0.6968
12	0.9955	0.9912	0.9840	0.9730	0.9573	0.9362	0.9091	0.8758	0.8364	0.7916
13	0.9983	0.9964	0.9929	0.9872	0.9784	0.9658	0.9486	0.9261	0.8981	0.8645
14	0.9994	0.9986	0.9970	0.9943	0.9897	0.9827	0.9726	0.9585	0.9400	0.9165
15	0.9998	0.9995	0.9988	0.9976	0.9954	0.9918	0.9862	0.9780	0.9665	0.9513
16	0.9999	0.9998	0.9996	0.9990	0.9980	0.9963	0.9934	0.9889	0.9823	0.9730
17	1.0000	0.9999	0.9998	0.9996	0.9992	0.9984	0.9970	0.9947	0.9911	0.9857
18	1.0000	1.0000	0.9999	0.9999	0.9997	0.9993	0.9987	0.9976	0.9957	0.9928
19	1.0000	1.0000	1.0000	1.0000	0.9999	0.9997	0.9995	0.9989	0.9980	0.9965
20	1.0000	1.0000	1.0000	1.0000	1.0000	0.9999	0.9998	0.9996	0.9991	0.9984
21	1.0000	1.0000	1.0000	1.0000	1.0000	1.0000	0.9999	0.9998	0.9996	0.9993
22	1.0000	1.0000	1.0000	1.0000	1.0000	1.0000	1.0000	0.9999	0.9999	0.9997

Table 3 The normal distribution function

The function tabulated below is $\Phi(z)$, defined as

$$\Phi(z) = \frac{1}{\sqrt{2\pi}} \int_{-\infty}^{z} e^{-\frac{1}{2}t^2} dt.$$

z	$\Phi(z)$	z	$\Phi(z)$	z	$\Phi(z)$	z	$\Phi(z)$	z	$\Phi(z)$
0.00	0.5000	0.50	0.6915	1.00	0.8413	1.50	0.9332	2.00	0.9772
0.01	0.5040	0.51	0.6950	1.01	0.8438	1.51	0.9345	2.02	0.9783
0.02	0.5080	0.52	0.6985	1.02	0.8461	1.52	0.9357	2.04	0.9793
0.03	0.5120	0.53	0.7019	1.03	0.8485	1.53	0.9370	2.06	0.9803
0.04	0.5160	0.54	0.7054	1.04	0.8508	1.54	0.9382	2.08	0.9812
0.05	0.5199	0.55	0.7088	1.05	0.8531	1.55	0.9394	2.10	0.9821
0.06	0.5239	0.56	0.7123	1.06	0.8554	1.56	0.9406	2.12	0.9830
0.07	0.5279	0.57	0.7157	1.07	0.8577	1.57	0.9418	2.14	0.9838
0.08	0.5319	0.58	0.7190	1.08	0.8599	1.58	0.9429	2.16	0.9846
0.09	0.5359	0.59	0.7224	1.09	0.8621	1.59	0.9441	2.18	0.9854
0.10	0.5398	0.60	0.7257	1.10	0.8643	1.60	0.9452	2.20	0.9861
0.11	0.5438	0.61	0.7291	1.11	0.8665	1.61	0.9463	2.22	0.9868
0.12	0.5478	0.62	0.7324	1.12	0.8686	1.62	0.9474	2.24	0.9875
0.13	0.5517	0.63	0.7357	1.13	0.8708	1.63	0.9484	2.26	0.9881
0.14	0.5557	0.64	0.7389	1.14	0.8729	1.64	0.9495	2.28	0.9887
0.15	0.5596	0.65	0.7422	1.15	0.8749	1.65	0.9505	2.30	0.9893
0.16	0.5636	0.66	0.7454	1.16	0.8770	1.66	0.9515	2.32	0.9898
0.17	0.5675	0.67	0.7486	1.17	0.8790	1.67	0.9525	2.34	0.9904
0.18	0.5714	0.68	0.7517	1.18	0.8810	1.68	0.9535	2.36	0.9909
0.19	0.5753	0.69	0.7549	1.19	0.8830	1.69	0.9545	2.38	0.9913
0.20	0.5793	0.70	0.7580	1.20	0.8849	1.70	0.9554	2.40	0.9918
0.21	0.5832	0.71	0.7611	1.21	0.8869	1.71	0.9564	2.42	0.9922
0.22	0.5871	0.72	0.7642	1.22	0.8888	1.72	0.9573	2.44	0.9927
0.23	0.5910	0.73	0.7673	1.23	0.8907	1.73	0.9582	2.46	0.9931
0.24	0.5948	0.74	0.7704	1.24	0.8925	1.74	0.9591	2.48	0.9934
0.25	0.5987	0.75	0.7734	1.25	0.8944	1.75	0.9599	2.50	0.9938
0.26	0.6026	0.76	0.7764	1.26	0.8962	1.76	0.9608	2.55	0.9946
0.27	0.6064	0.77	0.7794	1.27	0.8980	1.77	0.9616	2.60	0.9953
0.28	0.6103	0.78	0.7823	1.28	0.8997	1.78	0.9625	2.65	0.9960
0.29	0.6141	0.79	0.7852	1.29	0.9015	1.79	0.9633	2.70	0.9965
0.30	0.6179	0.80	0.7881	1.30	0.9032	1.80	0.9641	2.75	0.9970
0.31	0.6217	0.81	0.7910	1.31	0.9049	1.81	0.9649	2.80	0.9974
0.32	0.6255	0.82	0.7939	1.32	0.9066	1.82	0.9656	2.85	0.9978
0.33	0.6293	0.83	0.7967	1.33	0.9082	1.83	0.9664	2.90	0.9981
0.34	0.6331	0.84	0.7995	1.34	0.9099	1.84	0.9671	2.95	0.9984
0.35	0.6368	0.85	0.8023	1.35	0.9115	1.85	0.9678	3.00	0.9987
0.36	0.6406	0.86	0.8051	1.36	0.9131	1.86	0.9686	3.05	0.9989
0.37	0.6443	0.87	0.8078	1.37	0.9147	1.87	0.9693	3.10	0.9990
0.38	0.6480	0.88	0.8106	1.38	0.9162	1.88	0.9699	3.15	0.9992
0.39	0.6517	0.89	0.8133	1.39	0.9177	1.89	0.9706	3.20	0.9993
0.40	0.6554	0.90	0.8159	1.40	0.9192	1.90	0.9713	3.25	0.9994
0.41	0.6591	0.91	0.8186	1.41	0.9207	1.91	0.9719	3.30	0.9995
0.42	0.6628	0.92	0.8212	1.42	0.9222	1.92	0.9726	3.35	0.9996
0.43	0.6664	0.93	0.8238	1.43	0.9236	1.93	0.9732	3.40	0.9997
0.44	0.6700	0.94	0.8264	1.44	0.9251	1.94	0.9738	3.50	0.9998
0.45	0.6736	0.95	0.8289	1.45	0.9265	1.95	0.9744	3.60	0.9998
0.46	0.6772	0.96	0.8315	1.46	0.9279	1.96	0.9750	3.70	0.9999
0.47	0.6808	0.97	0.8340	1.47	0.9292	1.97	0.9756	3.80	0.9999
0.48	0.6844	0.98	0.8365	1.48	0.9306	1.98	0.9761	3.90	1.0000
0.49	0.6879	0.99	0.8389	1.49	0.9319	1.99	0.9767	4.00	1.0000
0.50	0.6915	1.00	0.8413	1.50	0.9332	2.00	0.9772		

Table 4 Percentage points of the normal distribution

The values z in the table are those which a random variable $Z \sim N(0, 1)$ exceeds with probability p; that is $P(Z > z) = 1 - \Phi(z) = p$.

p	z	p	z
05000	0.0000	0.0500	1.6449
0.4000	0.2533	0.0250	1.9600
0.3000	0.5244	0.0100	2.3263
0.2000	0.8416	0.0050	2.5758
0.1500	1.0364	0.0010	3.0902
0.1000	1.2816	0.0005	3.2905

Table 5 Percentage points of the χ^2 distribution

The values in the table are those which a random variable with the χ^2 distribution on v degrees of freedom exceeds with the probability shown.

v	0.995	0.990	0.975	0.950	0.900	0.100	0.050	0.025	0.010	0.005
1	0.000	0.000	0.001	0.004	0.016	2.705	3.841	5.024	6.635	7.879
2	0.010	0.020	0.051	0.103	0.211	4.605	5.991	7.378	9.210	10.597
3	0.072	0.115	0.216	0.352	0.584	6.251	7.815	9.348	11.345	12.838
4	0.207	0.297	0.484	0.711	1.064	7.779	9.488	11.143	13.277	14.860
5	0.412	0.554	0.831	1.145	1.610	9.236	11.070	12.832	15.086	16.750
6	0.676	0.872	1.237	1.635	2.204	10.645	12.592	14.449	16.812	18.548
7	0.989	1.239	1.690	2.167	2.833	12.017	14.067	16.013	18.475	20.278
8	1.344	1.646	2.180	2.733	3.490	13.362	15.507	17.535	20.090	21.955
9	1.735	2.088	2.700	3.325	4.168	14.684	16.919	19.023	21.666	23.589
10	2.156	2.558	3.247	3.940	4.865	15.987	18.307	20.483	23.209	25.188
11	2.603	3.053	3.816	4.575	5.580	17.275	19.675	21.920	24.725	26.757
12	3.074	3.571	4.404	5.226	6.304	18.549	21.026	23.337	26.217	28.300
13	3.565	4.107	5.009	5.892	7.042	19.812	22.362	24.736	27.688	29.819
14	4.075	4.660	5.629	6.571	7.790	21.064	23.685	26.119	29.141	31.319
15	4.601	5.229	6.262	7.261	8.547	22.307	24.996	27.488	30.578	32.801
16	5.142	5.812	6.908	7.962	9.312	23.542	26.296	28.845	32.000	34.267
17	5.697	6.408	7.564	8.672	10.085	24.769	27.587	30.191	33.409	35.718
18	6.265	7.015	8.231	9.390	10.865	25.989	28.869	31.526	34.805	37.156
19	6.844	7.633	8.907	10.117	11.651	27.204	30.144	32.852	36.191	38.582
20	7.434	8.260	9.591	10.851	12.443	28.412	31.410	34.170	37.566	39.997
21	8.034	8.897	10.283	11.591	13.240	29.615	32.671	35.479	38.932	41.401
22	8.643	9.542	10.982	12.338	14.042	30.813	33.924	36.781	40.289	42.796
23	9.260	10.196	11.689	13.091	14.848	32.007	35.172	38.076	41.638	44.181
24	9.886	10.856	12.401	13.848	15.659	33.196	36.415	39.364	42.980	45.558
25	10.520	11.524	13.120	14.611	16.473	34.382	37.652	40.646	44.314	46.928
26	11.160	12.198	13.844	15.379	17.292	35.563	38.885	41.923	45.642	48.290
27	11.808	12.879	14.573	16.151	18.114	36.741	40.113	43.194	46.963	49.645
28	12.461	13.565	15.308	16.928	18.939	37.916	41.337	44.461	48.278	50.993
29	13.121	14.256	16.047	17.708	19.768	39.088	42.557	45.722	49.588	52.336
30	13.787	14.953	16.791	18.493	20.599	40.256	43.773	46.979	50.892	53.672

Table 6 Critical values for correlation coefficients

These tables concern tests of the hypothesis that a population correlation coefficient ρ is 0. The values in the tables are the minimum values which need to be reached by a sample correlation coefficient in order to be significant at the level shown, on a one-tailed test.

Product-Moment Coefficient						Spearman's Coefficient		
		Level			Sample		Level	
0.10	0.05	0.025	0.01	0.005	Size	0.05	0.025	0.01
0.8000	0.9000	0.9500	0.9800	0.9900	4	1.0000	–	–
0.6870	0.8054	0.8783	0.9343	0.9587	5	0.9000	1.0000	1.0000
0.6084	0.7293	0.8114	0.8822	0.9172	6	0.8286	0.8857	0.9429
0.5509	0.6694	0.7545	0.8329	0.8745	7	0.7143	0.7857	0.8929
0.5067	0.6215	0.7067	0.7887	0.8343	8	0.6429	0.7381	0.8333
0.4716	0.5822	0.6664	0.7498	0.7977	9	0.6000	0.7000	0.7833
0.4428	0.5494	0.6319	0.7155	0.7646	10	0.5636	0.6485	0.7455
0.4187	0.5214	0.6021	0.6851	0.7348	11	0.5364	0.6182	0.7091
0.3981	0.4973	0.5760	0.6581	0.7079	12	0.5035	0.5874	0.6783
0.3802	0.4762	0.5529	0.6339	0.6835	13	0.4835	0.5604	0.6484
0.3646	0.4575	0.5324	0.6120	0.6614	14	0.4637	0.5385	0.6264
0.3507	0.4409	0.5140	0.5923	0.6411	15	0.4464	0.5214	0.6036
03383	0.4259	0.4973	0.5742	0.6226	16	0.4294	0.5029	0.5824
0.3271	0.4124	0.4821	0.5577	0.6055	17	0.4142	0.4877	0.5662
0.3170	0.4000	0.4683	0.5425	0.5897	18	0.4014	0.4716	0.5501
0.3077	0.3887	0.4555	0.5285	0.5751	19	0.3912	0.4596	0.5351
0.2992	0.3783	0.4438	0.5155	0.5614	20	0.3805	0.4466	0.5218
0.2914	0.3687	0.4329	0.5034	0.5487	21	0.3701	0.4364	0.5091
0.2841	0.3598	0.4227	0.4921	0.5368	22	0.3608	0.4252	0.4975
0.2774	0.3515	0.4133	0.4815	0.5256	23	0.3528	0.4160	0.4862
0.2711	0.3438	0.4044	0.4716	0.5151	24	0.3443	0.4070	0.4757
0.2653	0.3365	0.3961	0.4622	0.5052	25	0.3369	0.3977	0.4662
0.2598	0.3297	0.3882	0.4534	0.4958	26	0.3306	0.3901	0.4571
0.2546	0.3233	0.3809	0.4451	0.4869	27	0.3242	0.3828	0.4487
0.2497	0.3172	0.3739	0.4372	0.4785	28	0.3180	0.3755	0.4401
0.2451	0.3115	0.3673	0.4297	0.4705	29	0.3118	0.3685	0.4325
0.2407	0.3061	0.3610	0.4226	0.4629	30	0.3063	0.3624	0.4251
0.2070	0.2638	0.3120	0.3665	0.4026	40	0.2640	0.3128	0.3681
0.1843	0.2353	0.2787	0.3281	0.3610	50	0.2353	0.2791	0.3293
0.1678	0.2144	0.2542	0.2997	0.3301	60	0.2144	0.2545	0.3005
0.1550	0.1982	0.2352	0.2776	0.3060	70	0.1982	0.2354	0.2782
0.1448	0.1852	0.2199	0.2597	0.2864	80	0.1852	0.2201	0.2602
0.1364	0.1745	0.2072	0.2449	0.2702	90	0.1745	0.2074	0.2453
0.1292	0.1654	0.1966	0.2324	0.2565	100	0.1654	0.1967	0.2327

Table 7 Random numbers

86 13	84 10	07 30	39 05	97 96	88 07	37 26	04 89	13 48	19 20
60 78	48 12	99 47	09 46	91 33	17 21	03 94	79 00	08 50	40 16
78 48	06 37	82 26	01 06	64 65	94 41	17 26	74 66	61 93	24 97
80 56	90 79	66 94	18 40	97 79	93 20	41 51	25 04	20 71	76 04
99 09	39 25	66 31	70 56	30 15	52 17	87 55	31 11	10 68	98 23
56 32	32 72	91 65	97 36	56 61	12 79	95 17	57 16	53 58	96 36
66 02	49 93	97 44	99 15	56 86	80 57	11 78	40 23	58 40	86 14
31 77	53 94	05 93	56 14	71 23	60 46	05 33	23 72	93 10	81 23
98 79	72 43	14 76	54 77	66 29	84 09	88 56	75 86	41 67	04 42
50 97	92 15	10 01	57 01	87 33	73 17	70 18	40 21	24 20	66 62
90 51	94 50	12 48	88 95	09 34	09 30	22 27	25 56	40 76	01 59
31 99	52 24	13 43	27 88	11 39	41 65	00 84	13 06	31 79	74 97
22 96	23 34	46 12	67 11	48 06	99 24	14 83	78 37	65 73	39 47
06 84	55 41	27 06	74 59	14 29	20 14	45 75	31 16	05 41	22 96
08 64	89 30	25 25	71 35	33 31	04 56	12 67	03 74	07 16	49 32
86 87	62 43	15 11	76 49	79 13	78 80	93 89	09 57	07 14	40 74
94 44	97 13	77 04	35 02	12 76	60 91	93 40	81 06	85 85	72 84
63 25	55 14	66 47	99 90	02 90	83 43	16 01	19 69	11 78	87 16
11 22	83 98	15 21	18 57	53 42	91 91	26 52	89 13	86 00	47 61
01 70	10 83	94 71	13 67	11 12	36 54	53 32	90 43	79 01	95 15

Answers

The University of London Examination and Assessment Council accepts no responsibility whatsoever for the accuracy or method of working in the answers given for examination questions.

Exercise 1A

In this exercise there are several possible answers to each question. Brief suggestions are given – more detail would be needed for a full answer.

1 The selection of individual elements of a population. Advantages: low cost, often more reliable, represents whole population.

2 Every item is observed/measured.
e.g. National Census: for forecasting school places
Nursery School: numbers of carriers of a virus.

3 harness destroyed in testing.

4 (a) cheaper, quicker
(b) sampling units used to represent the population – may be the whole or part of the population
(c) none
(d) variable population requires a larger sampling frame than a non-variable one

5 (a) Each sample of size n has the same chance of being selected; each member of the total population has an equal chance of selection; sometimes difficult for large populations; easy to use.
(b) Population divided into mutually exclusive groups – equal proportions of each group sampled; good for easily stratified populations – some problems possible within strata.
(c) Choosing at regular intervals from an ordered list; good for large populations and easy to use; bias in ordered list can be a problem.

6 (a) 01, 06, 64, 65, 94, 41 or 01, 18, 70, 97, 99, 56; others possible
(b) 079, 056, 110, 086, 143, 108 or 136, 097, 148, 069, 137, 123; others possible
(c) 010, 441, 172, 193, 249, 569 or 010, 184, 561, 547, 570, 278

7 electoral role: could use systematic sampling

8 divides population into mutually exclusive groups

9 (a) Systematic sampling would be easy to use.
(b) The ordered list would need to be truly random.

10 (a) stratified – 3 strata

(b) possibly questionnaire to 10% of each strata

(c) advantages: information on each strata, probably quite accurate

11 (a) (i) cost, reliability

(ii) list of sampling units used to represent the population

(b) many possible answers, e.g.

(i) shoppers at a supermarket when considering shopping

(ii) students in a secondary school when looking into views on school meals

Exercise 2A

1 (a) Yes (b) Yes (c) No (d) Yes
(e) No (f) No (g) Yes

2 (i) (a) $N(10\mu, 10\sigma^2)$

(b) $N\left(\mu, \frac{13\sigma^2}{25}\right)$ (c) $N(0, 10\sigma^2)$

(d) $N\left(\mu, \frac{\sigma^2}{10}\right)$ (e) $N(0, 10\sigma^2)$

(f) N(0, 10)

(i) (a) Yes (b) Yes (c) No
(d) Yes (e) Yes (f) No

3 (a) $B(20, 0.05)$ (b) 0.9245
(c) 1, 0.95 (d) 1, 0.0475

4 (a) $B(20, p)$
(b) $(1-p)^{20} + 20(1-p)^{19}p + 190(1-p)^{18}p^2$
(c) $\mu = 20p, \sigma^2 = 20p(1-p)$
(d) $\mu = 20p, \sigma^2 = p(1-p)$

5 (a) $B(10, \frac{1}{4})$ (b) 0.5256, 0.0035
(c) 2.5, 1.875 (d) 2.5, 0.1875

6 (a) $\mu = 3\frac{5}{6}, \sigma^2 = 10.81$
(b) {1,1}; {5,5}; {10,10}; {1,5}; {5,10}; {1,10}
(c)

$\bar{X}$:	1	3	5	5.5	7.5	10
$p(\bar{x})$:	$\frac{9}{36}$	$\frac{12}{36}$	$\frac{4}{36}$	$\frac{6}{36}$	$\frac{4}{36}$	$\frac{1}{36}$

(d) $\frac{23}{6}, \frac{389}{72}$

7 (a) $6\frac{1}{4}, \frac{75}{16}$
(b) (5,5,5)
(5,5,10) : (5,10,5) : (10,5,5)
(5,10,10) : (10,5,10) : (10,10,5)
(10,10,10)
(c)

$\bar{X}$	: 5	$\frac{20}{3}$	$\frac{25}{3}$	10
$p(\bar{x})$	: $\frac{27}{64}$	$\frac{27}{64}$	$\frac{9}{64}$	$\frac{1}{64}$

(d) $6\frac{1}{4}, \frac{75}{32}$
(e)

M	: 5	10
$p(m)$	: $\frac{27}{32}$	$\frac{5}{32}$

(f) $\frac{185}{32}$, 3.296

8 (a) $1, \frac{1}{2}$
(b) {0,0,0}; {0,0,1}; {0,0,2}; {0,1,2}; {1,1,1}; {1,2,2}; {1,1,2}; {2,2,2}; {0,1,1}
{0,2,2}
(c)

$\bar{X}$	: 0	$\frac{1}{3}$	$\frac{2}{3}$	1	$\frac{4}{3}$	$\frac{5}{3}$	2
$p(\bar{x})$	: $\frac{1}{64}$	$\frac{6}{64}$	$\frac{15}{64}$	$\frac{20}{64}$	$\frac{15}{64}$	$\frac{6}{64}$	$\frac{1}{64}$

(d) $1, \frac{1}{6}$
(e)

N	:	0	1	2
$p(n)$	:	$\frac{10}{64}$	$\frac{44}{64}$	$\frac{10}{64}$

(f) $1, \frac{5}{16}$

Exercise 2B

1 (a) 19.3, 3.98
(b) 3.375, 4.65
(c) 223.0, 7174.12
(d) 0.5833, 0.027

2 (a) 0.533 (b) 0.539 (c) 28.233
(d) 0.0519

3 (a) 36.4, 29.17 (b) 9, 4
(c) 1.1, 0.0225
(d) 11.2, 2.24

4 (a) 0.493 (b) 0.365 (c) 0.00466
(d) 0.387

5 (a) 16.2, 12.03 (b) 15.92, 10.34

(c) 0.63, 0.63, 0.45

(d) Combined since s.e. is smaller.

6 (a) 65, 9.74 (b) 37 or more

(c) 65.56

7 28

8 (a) 4.89 (b) 35 or more

9 (a) $np, 2np, np(1-p), 2np(1-p)$

(b) Prefer $\frac{X_2}{2n}$ since variance is smaller

(e) Y (f) $\frac{p}{3}$

10 (d) $\left(\frac{n}{m+n}\right)\bar{X}+\left(\frac{m}{m+n}\right)\bar{Y}$

11 (a) $\frac{\alpha}{2}$ (b) $2\bar{X}$ (c) $\frac{\alpha}{\sqrt{3n}}$

12 97

13 236, 7.58

14 205.16, 9.22

Exercise 2C

1 0.0071

2 (a) 0.25 (b) 0.010

3 (a) 0.067 (b) At least 241

4 (a) 2; 0.5 (b) 0.19

5 (a) 0.04 (b) 0.01

6 0.11

7 0.06

8 (a) 0.002 (b) 0.04

9 1936

10 0.020

11 (a) 0.14 (b) 312

Exercise 2D

1 (a) (124.08, 131.92)

(b) (122.85, 133.15)

2 (a) (83.68, 86.32) (b) (83.43, 86.57)

3 (20.56, 25.44)

4 (a) 609 (b) 865 (c) 1493

5 (a) 98 (b) 139 (c) 239

6 (1.765, 2.039)

7 (304.2, 315.8)

8 (73 113, 78 631)

9 (a) Simple random sample

(b) (66.73, 70.07)

(c) Sample is not representative. The examiner marked some good candidates.

10 (b) (77.67, 79.73)

11 (a) (23.2, 26.8), since it is the narrowest.

(b) 0.9

(c) 25

12 (a) (83.33, 87.27) (b) (82.51, 88.09)

(c) (82.21, 88.39)

13 (a) £135, (130,140) (b) 85%

(c) 189

14 (30.4, 32.4)

15 (257.855, 274.145)

16 0.311, 0.866, (21.75, 23.31)

Exercise 2E

1 $z = 0.596$, not sig.

2 $z = -1.8$, sig.

3 $z = 1.83$, not sig.

4 $z = 2.71$, sig.

5 $z = -2.13$, not sig.

6 $\bar{X} \leqslant 119.40$

7 $\bar{X} \geqslant 13.20$

8 $\bar{X} \leqslant 84.28$

9 $\bar{X} \geqslant 0.877$ or $\bar{X} \leqslant -0.877$

10 $\bar{X} \geqslant -7.31$ or $\bar{X} \leqslant -8.69$

11 $z = -2$, sig, there is evidence of an improvement.

12 $z = 1.667$, sig., there is evidence that it improves IQ score.

13 $z = -1.826$, not sig., no evidence that diameter has altered.

14 $\bar{x} = 11.2, s^2 = 2.54, 0.0241$, reject H_0

15 $z = -2.87$ Average lifetime is different.

Exercise 2F

1 $z = 1.370$, not sig.

2 $z = -1.996$, sig.

3 $z = -2.395$, sig.

4 $z = 2.712$, sig., central limit theorem for $\bar{X}_i \sim$ Normal

5 $z = 1.396$, not sig., central limit theorem for $\bar{X}_i \sim$ Normal

6 $z = -2.529$, sig., central limit theorem for $\bar{X}_i \sim$ Normal

7 $z = 1.345$, not sig., no evidence that pipe length has changed.

8 (a) $z = -2.054$, sig.; evidence of a difference in ages.
(b) Assume $s_1 = \sigma_1$, $s_2 = \sigma_2$ and use central limit theorem.

9 (a) $z = -1.694$, not sig., no evidence of a change in mean.
(b) Assume $\sigma = s$ and use central limit theorem.

10 (a) $z = 2.645$, sig., evidence that new bands are better.
(b) (46.67, 47.63)

11 Complaint justified, (8.19, 8.53)

12 $\bar{x} = 4.53, s^2 = 3.3891,$
$\frac{s}{\sqrt{n}} = 0.184, (4.10, 4.96), 0.352$

13 $\bar{x} = 14.01, \frac{s}{\sqrt{n}} = 0.040, (13.92, 14.10), 0.40$

Exercise 2G

1 (a) C.R. $\bar{x} \geqslant 51.56..$, reject H_0, 0.016
(b) C.R. $\bar{x} \leqslant 43.82..$, not sig, 0.991
(c) C.R. $\bar{x} \leqslant 20.34$ or $\bar{x} \geqslant 20.66$, sig, 0.776
(d) C.R. $\bar{x} \leqslant 28.85$ or $\bar{x} \geqslant 31.15$, not sig, 0.029

2 (a) $z = -2$, sig.
(b) (i) 0 (ii) 0.0004 (iii) 0.95 (iv) 1
(c) $z = -2$, not sig. (i) 0 (ii) 0.0037 (iii) 0.99 (iv) 1

3 (a) $z = -1.5$, not sig.
(b) $\bar{x} \geqslant 20.78$ or $\bar{x} \leqslant 19.22$
(c) 0.295

4 (a) 64.51
(b) sig, organisation should recommend the chair.
(c) 0.428
(d) Manufacturer wants P(type II error) lower. If the chair works then the probability of not rejecting H_0 (i.e. saying the chair does *not* work) is small.
(e) e.g. Double n to 60
P(type II error) $= 0.174$

Exercise 2H

1 0.0781, not sig.

2 0.0464, sig.

3 0.0480, sig.

4 0.0049, sig.

5 0.2632, not sig.

6 $X \geqslant 5$, 0.0328

7 $X = 0$, 0.0388

8 $X \geqslant 8$, 0.0048

9 $X \leqslant 3$ or $X \geqslant 13$, 0.037

10 $X \geqslant 7$, 0.0024

11 0.8497

12 0.8784

13 0.9726

14 0.9496

15 0.9781

16 0.1875, not sig., manufacturer not justified.

17 0.1154, not sig., no evidence of bias

18 $X \leqslant 6$

19 0.3813, not sig., no evidence probability is less than $\frac{1}{6}$

20 $z = -1.170$, not sig., evidence Blue party overstating their support.

21 $X \geqslant 137$ or 138, reject H_0 and conclude that the proportion with unsafe brakes is > 0.15.

22 $z = -2.80$, sig., students may come from a deprived area.

23 (a) 0.395 (b) 0.865, $p = 0.14$, cannot reject claim

24 (b) 0.218 (c) no evidence of an increase

25 (a) 0.091, sig.
(b) $z = 1.27$, not sig.

Exercise 2I

1 0.0424, sig.

2 0.0430, not sig.

3 0.1905, not sig.

4 $X \geqslant 9$

5 $X \leqslant 2$

6 $X = 0$

0.0214, 0.8944

8 0.0062, 0.9797

9 0.0302, 0.9179

10 0.1321, not sig., no evidence of a decrease

11 0.124, new schedules do not appear to have increased the average number of late buses.

Review Exercise 1

1 (a) (i) Advantage: very accurate; disadvantage: expensive
(ii) Advantage: easier data collection; disadvantage: bias possible
(b) Number each element of population – use random number table to select 100.

2 (a) A sample size n is drawn from a population size N in such a way that every member of N has an equal chance of being selected.
Advantage: free from bias; disadvantage: difficult with large sample
(b) choosing at regular intervals from an ordered list
Advantage: simple; disadvantage: bias if list not truly random

3 All elements have an equal chance of selection.
(b) is best: (a) is biased – only people shopping in that street at that time are sampled.
(a) easy but biased, (b) reliable but time-consuming

4 Stratified – gives all groups an equal chance to give their views.

5 Population divided into mutually exclusive strata – equal proportions of each strata sampled; useful for large populations with clearly defined groups.
Advantages: gives information on individual strata as well as whole; often very accurate
Disadvantages: strata are sometimes difficult to define; problems can arise when sampling within the individual strata

6 (a) 13.09 (b) (36.6, 37.8)
(c) (1.12, 3.28)
(d) difference not solely due to chance

7 (a) 6.8, 5.89 (b) 7.15, 6.34
(c) second jet, larger number of observations

8 (a) 0.433 (b) 0.184 (c) 0.021
(d) H_0: $\lambda = 4$; H_1: $\lambda > 4$
(e) $\lambda \geqslant 8$; 0.051 (f) Do not reject H_0

9 (b) 28 or more.

10 (a) $H_0 : \mu = 9$; $H_1 : \mu < 9$
(b) $x \leqslant 4, 0.055$
(c) Do not reject H_0.

11 (a) (£3.37, £14.07) (b) (£9.07, £10.35)
Reject H_0; $n = 163$

12 (a) 0.182; (9.84, 10.56) (b) 13

13 (b) 0.256 (c) 0.057
(d) reduction in number of lorries pulling in

14 (a) Prob. = 0.118 – cannot say proportion is reduced.
(b) Prob. = 0.0748 – cannot say proportion has changed.

15 31

16 0.110; 0.002; weekly distance reduced

17 (a) 0.034 (b) 0.069 (not significant)

18 insufficient evidence that machine is not fulfilling (a)

19 (i) (a) approx normal (b) normal
(ii) (a) (£17.67, £19.33) (b) 278
(c) £19.40 outside interval – evidence of a difference.

20 82.78; (0.823, 0.845); 0.834 is in interval – no evidence of malfunctioning

21 (a) 0.845; mean appears to be higher
(b) $\bar{x} = 0.2$ prob. = 0.001 15, sig. line probably needs more protection

Exercise 3A

1 (a) $r = 0.577...[S_{xy} = 620, S_{yy} = 826, S_{xx} = 1396.83]$
(b) $r = 0.108...[S_{xy} = 88.516, S_{yy} = 646.902, S_{xx} = 1034.509]$
(c) $r = 0.481...[S_{xy} = 6.2886, S_{yy} = 38.989, S_{xx} = 4.3759]$

2 (a) $r = 0.9739...[S_{xy} = 56.935, S_{yy} = 223.135, S_{xx} = 15.315]$
(b) $r = -0.974...[S_{xy} = -5342.64, S_{yy} = 860.727, S_{xx} = 34\,936.19]$

3 (a) $r = 0.951...$
(b) $r = -0.978...$
(c) $r = 0.7589...$

4 $H_0 : \rho = 0; H_1 : \rho \neq 0$
(a) Critical values ± 0.3120. Reject H_0.
(b) Critical values ± 0.3665. Do not reject H_0.

5 (a) $S_{xx} = 10.857\,14, S_{yy} = 28, S_{xy} = -17, r = -0.975...$
(b) Assume data are jointly normally distributed. Critical values ± 0.8745. Reject H_0: there is a correlation between x and y.

6 (a) (i) none (ii) none
(b) $r = 0.9417...$ On this evidence we can support the statement.
$[S_{xy} = 1029.286, S_{yy} = 745.714, S_{xx} = 1601.714]$..

7 (a) $S_{xx} = 19.1819, S_{yy} = 172\,234.9, S_{xy} = 1231.27, r = 0.677...$
(b) Assume data are jointly normally distributed. $H_0 : \rho = 0; H_1 : \rho > 0$; 5% critical value is 0.5214. Reject H_0. There is evidence to suggest that the taller you are the more you weigh.

8 (a) $S_{xx} = 1.2889..., S_{yy} = 8.316\,01, S_{xy} = -1.828..., r = -0.558...$
(b) There is minimal evidence to suggest that as unemployment increases wage inflation decreases.

9 (a) $R = 0.4726...$
(b) $r = 0.4663...$
There is slight evidence to suggest that blood pressure rises as weight and age increase.

10 (b) (i) $S_{tp} = 255$ (ii) $r = 0.9354...$
(c) $H_0 : \rho = 0; H_1 : \rho > 0;$
Critical value $= 0.4973$
Reject H_0: there is reason to believe that students who do well in theoretical Biology are likely to do well in practical Biology.

11 $r = 0.8349...[S_{xx} = 82.5, S_{yy} = 32.900, S_{xy} = 43.5]$
There is some evidence of linear relationship. The older the trainee the longer it is likely to take to train him/her.

Exercise 3B

1 (a) $\Sigma d^2 = 10, r_s = 0.714....$ limited evidence of positive correlation
(b) $\Sigma d^2 = 18, r_s = 0.8909....$ evidence of positive correlation
(c) $\Sigma d^2 = 158, r_s = -0.8809...$ evidence of negative correlation

2 (a) $\Sigma d^2 = 48$
(b) $r_s = 0.832...$ The more goals a team scores the higher they are likely to be in the league table.

3 (a) $\Sigma d^2 = 68$
(b) $r_s = 0.190...$ The teachers need to rethink their grading procedures. There is very little agreement between them.

4 $\Sigma d^2 = 20, r_s = 0.7619....$ The trainee vet is doing quite well. There is a fair degree of agreement between the trainee vet and the qualified vet. The trainee still has more to learn.

5 (a) The marks are subjective judgements.
(b) $\Sigma d^2 = 28, r_s = 0.8303....$
There is a fair degree of agreement between judges.

6 (a) Spearman's rank, because he is concerned with order.
(b) $\Sigma d^2 = 100, r_s = 0.3939...$
There is little correlation between the predicted and actual order.

7 (a) $\Sigma d^2 = 30$
(b) $r_s = 0.464...$ There appears to be some positive agreement between the number of years a patient has smoked and lung damage but it is not very strong. It would appear that other factors need to be considered.

8 $\Sigma d^2 = 76, r_s = -0.357...H_0 : \rho = 0;$
$H_1 : \rho < 0$. Critical value 0.8929. There is no reason to reject H_0.

9 $H_0 : \rho = 0; H_1 : \rho \neq 0$. Critical values ± 0.3624. Reject H_0 : There is reason to believe that engine size and fuel consumption are related.

10 (a) $\Sigma d^2 = 8, r_s = 0.771...$
(b) $H_0 : \rho = 0; H_1 : \rho > 0$. Critical value 0.8286 No reason to reject H_0. On this evidence the assertion is not correct.

11 (a) $\Sigma d^2 = 58, r_s = 0.797...$
(b) $H_0 : \rho = 0; H_1 : \rho \neq 0$. Critical values ± 0.5874. Reject H_0: On this evidence it would seem that students who do well in Mathematics are likely to do well in Music.

12 (a) $\Sigma d^2 = 54, r_s = 0.6727....$
(b) $H_0 : \rho = 0; H_1 : \rho \neq 0$. Critical values ± 0.6485. Reject H_0: the child shows some ability in this task.

13 (a) $\Sigma d^2 = 64, r_s 0.8285...$
(b) $H_0 : \rho = 0; H_1 : \rho \neq 0$. Critical values ± 0.8857. Do not reject H_0: the

coefficient is close to the critical value. More samples should be taken if you wish to be confident in your findings.

Exercise 4A

1 $S_{xy} = 69.5999, S_{xx} = 40.7999,$
$y = 1.7059x - 0.2941$

2 $S_{xy} = 14.5, S_{xx} = 10, y = 1.45x - 0.07$

3 (a) $\bar{x} = 10, \bar{y} = 110.2, S_{xy} = 86, S_{xx} = 40$
$y - 110.2 = 2.15(x - 10)$

4 (a) negative linear
(b) $S_{xy} = -280, S_{xx} = 2800, \bar{y} = 12.9714,$
$\bar{x} = 40, y = 16.9714 - 0.1x$

5 $S_{HT} = 9.664, S_{TT} = 6.12,$
$H = 1.58T - 11.03,$
$H = 1.3$ when $T = 7.8$

6 (a) Linear relationship, number of items fixed
(b) $S_{xy} = 6344,\ S_{xx} = 6486,\ \bar{y} = 65,$
$\bar{x} = 45, y = 0.978x + 20.985$
(c) 17,172; break-even point

7 (a) $S_{xy} = -3243.533,\ S_{xx} = 1049.78$
$y = 55.52 - 3.0898x, h = 217.321 + 3.09s$
(b) Every extra rev/min reduces the life of the drill by just over 3 hours.
(c) 124.62 hours

8 $\bar{A} = 5.5, \bar{S} = 0.2732, S = 0.694 + 0.014A,$
0.744

9 $S_{TH} = 1200, S_{TT} = 150\,000,$
$H = 0.008T - 0.8$, 0.8 units $\{100 \times \beta\}$

10 (b) $S_{y\frac{1}{x}} = -1.450\,45, S_{\left(\frac{1}{x}\frac{1}{x}\right)} = 136.18$
$y = 0.232 - \frac{0.011}{x}$

11 (a) $S_{xy} = 3477.6, S_{xx} = 4402$
$y = 0.16 + 0.79x$
(b) The amount of extra food per extra hen
(c) £11.43

12 $\bar{T} = 17.5, \bar{A} = 14.875$
$A = 6.30 + 0.49T$
When $T = 20, A = 16.1$. Both observed values have errors in them.
0.49 grams
$T = 0$ is outside the range of the experimental results. This means the value of A would not be reliable.

Exercise 5A

[Null and Alternative hypotheses should always be stated in a test. They are not always given in these answers.]

1 (a) Expected value 20,
$\chi_7^2(5\%) = 14.067, \chi^2 = 6.4$
No reason to reject H_0.
(b) The values would appear to be modelled by a discrete uniform distribution.

2 (a) $\chi_4^2(5\%) = 9.488, \chi^2 = 4.49$
No reason to reject H_0. The binomial distribution could be a suitable model.
(b) Work out λ calculated from the observed frequencies and use this to work out the probabilities.

3 (a) H_0: the data are modelled by Po(2).
$\chi_5^2(5\%) = 11.070, \chi^2 = 4.10$
No reason to reject H_0.
(b) reduction by 1

4 Expected values 17, H_0: deliveries are uniformly distributed.
$\chi_5^2(5\%) = 11.070, \chi^2 = 5.765$
No reason to reject H_0.

5 (a) 1.4
(b) $\chi_2^2(10\%) = 4.605, \chi^2 = 5.04$
Reject H_0. These data do not come from a Poisson distribution with $\lambda = 1.4$.

6 (a) 0.4 (b) $\chi_2^2(5\%) = 5.991, \chi^2 = 3.19$
No reason to reject H_0

7 Expected values: 21.6, 16.2, 27, 5.4, 10.8
$\chi_4^2(5\%) = 9.488, \chi^2 = 1.84$
No reason to reject H_0. The number of accidents might well be constant at each factory.

8 $\lambda = 3.45, \chi_4^2(5\%) = 9.488, \chi^2 = 0.99$
No reason to reject H_0. There is not sufficient evidence to suggest the data are not modelled by Po(3.45).

9 (a) Breakdowns are independent of each other, occur singly and at a constant rate.
(b) $\lambda = 0.95, H_0$: the data can be modelled by Po(0.95)
Expected values: 38.67, 36.74, 17.45, 5.52, 7.14
$\chi_2^2(5\%) = 5.991, \chi^2 = 16.04$.
Reject H_0. The breakdowns are not modelled by Po(0.9).

10 H_0 : prizes are uniformly distributed
H_1: prizes are not uniformly distributed
$\chi_9^2(5\%) = 16.919, \chi^2 = 10.74$
Do not reject H_0. There is no reason to believe the distribution of prizes is not uniform.

Exercise 5B

[Interpolation has been used in most answers. Answers that do not use interpolation are acceptable.]

1 $\chi_7^2(5\%) = 14.067, \chi^2 = 4.16$
H_0: the data can be modelled by a continuous uniform distribution.
No reason to reject H_0.

2 $\chi_2^2(5\%) = 5.991, \chi^2 = 4.58$
No reason to reject H_0. No reason to believe N $(3.8, 0.5^2)$ is not a suitable model.

3 $\chi_2^2(5\%) = 5.991, \chi^2 = 0.29$
No reason to reject H_0. $N(58, 4^2)$ might well be a suitable model.

4 $\chi_2^2(5\%) = 5.991, \chi^2 = 3.20$
No reason to reject H_0. No evidence to suggest $N(8, 0.9^2)$ is not a suitable model.

5 (a) $\chi_2^2(1\%) = 9.210, \chi^2 = 4.93$
$\mu = 23.4, \sigma = 10.222$
Do not reject H_0. The data could come from a $N(23.4, 10.222^2)$ distribution.
(b) Shopkeeper could use this to help with stock control.

6 (a) $\chi_5^2(2\frac{1}{2}\%) = 12.832, \chi^2 = 44.314$
Reject H_0. The data cannot be modelled by N(1.32, 0.0016).
(b) $\mu = 1.3165, \sigma = 0.0569$,
$\chi_5^2(2\frac{1}{2}\%) = 12.832, \chi^2 = 5.78$ to 5.85
Accept H_0.
(c) The best model is $N(1.3165, 0.0569^2)$.
175, 425, 425, 175.

7 H_0: Trees have their branches uniformly arranged around the trunk
open: $\chi^2 = 5.248, \chi_7^2(5\%) = 14.067$
Accept H_0
edge: $\chi^2 = 23.456, \chi_7^2(5\%) = 14.067$
Reject H_0
Trees grown in open have branches continuously uniformly distributed. Those grown at the edge do not. Branches tend to grow on the side nearest the light.

Exercise 5C

1 $\nu = 2, \chi_2^2(5\%) = 5.991$

2 H_0: Ownership is not related to locality
H_1: Ownership is related to locality
$\nu = 2, \chi_2^2(5\%) = 5.991, \chi^2 = 13.1$
Reject H_0.

3 (a) $(3-1)(3-1) = 4$
(b) $\chi_4^2(5\%) = 9.488$.
Reject H_0. There is an association between groups and grades.

4 H_0: There is no relationship between results
$\chi_4^2(5\%) = 9.488, \chi^2 = 8.56$
Do not reject H_0. There is no reason to believe there is a relationship between results

5 $\chi_2^2(5\%) = 5.991, \chi^2 = 1.757$
Do not reject H_0. There is no evidence to suggest association between station and lateness.

6 $\chi_4^2(1\%) = 13.277$
Reject H_0. Sex and grade appear to be associated.

7 (a)

	A	*B*	
OK	52	34	86
Def.	8	6	14
	60	40	100

(b) $\chi_1^2(0.05) = 3.841, \chi^2 = 0.0035$
Do not reject H_0. There appears to be no association between factory and number of defects.

8 (a)

	Boys	*Girls*	
Flu	15	8	23
No flu	7	20	27
	22	28	50

$\chi_1^2(5\%) = 3.841, \chi^2 = 6.269$
Reject H_0. There is an association between sex and susceptibility to influenza.

9 $\chi_2^2(5\%) = 5.991, \chi^2 = 27.27$
Reject H_0. There is a difference in beaches with regard to male and female organisms.

10 $\chi_1^2(5\%) = 3.841, \chi^2 = 7.39$
Reject H_0. There is an association between age and the number of credit cards possessed.

Review exercise 2

1 23.209

2 $H_0 : \rho = 0, H_1 : \rho \neq 0$, critical value $= 0.7857$
Reject H_0. Correspondence exists between ranks.

3 15.507

4 $\nu = 8$, critical region $\chi^2 \geqslant 15.507$

5 (a) $\Sigma d^2 = 36, r_s = 0.5714...$
(b) $H_0 : \rho = 0, H_1 : \rho \neq 0$
No reason to reject H_0. Students who do well in Geography do not necessarily do well in Statistics.

6 $S_{TE} = 1200, S_{TT} = 150\,000, \bar{E} = 1.6$
$\bar{T} = 500, E = 0.008T - 2.4$, 1.04 mm

7 $\nu = 6, 12.592$

8 $\lambda = 0.654, \nu = 2, \chi^2 = 21.506$,
$\chi_2^2(5\%) = 5.991$ Reject H_0.
A Po (0.654) distribution is not a suitable model.

9 (a) $\Sigma d^2 = 24, r_s = 0.3142...$
(b) Critical value $= 0.8286$,
$H_0 : \rho = 0, H_1 : \rho > 0$.

Do not reject H_0. There appears to be no agreement between the ranks.

10 (a) x is independent, y is dependent.
(b) $S_{LW} = 178.4397, S_{LL} = 143.3174,$
$S_{WW} = 231.72$, $r = 0.9791...$ This is close to $+1$ so there is a strong positive linear association between the length and width of this species of fossil.

11 $\chi^2_5(5\%) = 11.070, \chi^2 = 22.7$
Reject H_0. $N(160, 16^2)$ is not a good model.

12 $\chi^2_1(5\%) = 3.841, \chi^2 = 0.052$
No reason to reject H_0. The fish could have come from the same population.

13 H_0: The proportions in both schools are the same.
H_1: The proportions in both schools are not the same. $\chi^2_2(5\%) = 5.991, \chi^2 = 1.038$
Do not reject H_0. On this evidence there is no reason to believe the proportions are not the same.

14 H_0: There is no association between type of book and cover.
H_1: There is association between type of book and cover.
$\chi^2_2(5\%) = 5.991, \chi^2 = 11.08$
Reject H_0. There is association between type of book and cover.

15

	Yes	*No*	
Sample 1	62	38	100
Sample 2	56	24	80
	118	62	180

$\chi^2_1(5\%) = 3.841, \chi^2 = 0.93$. Do not reject H_0. There is no evidence to show brand X has altered.

16 (a) $\mu = 32.9\%$
(b) $\chi^2_2(5\%) = 5.991, \chi^2 = 0.49$.
Do not reject H_0. It would appear that the iron content can be modelled by $N(32.9, 2.023^2)$.

17 (a) $S_{xx} = 1038.1, S_{yy} = 340.4004,$
$S_{xy} = 202.2002$, $r = 0.340...$
(b) (i) one or both given in rank order
(ii)a significance test on r is required and population is not normal.
(c) $\Sigma d^2 = 112, r_s = 0.321....$
(d) $H_0{:}\rho = 0$, $H_1{:}\rho \neq 0$, critical value 0.5636
Do not reject H_0

18 $\chi^2_1(5\%) = 3.841, \chi^2 = 0.6$
No reason to reject H_0. There is no evidence to suggest association between left-handedness and sex.

19 (b) $S_{xx} = 6908.1, S_{yy} = 50\,288.1,$
$S_{xy} = 17\,461.9$, $r = 0.9368....$
(c) $\Sigma d^2 = 4$, $r_s = 0.976....$
(d) product-moment correlation coefficient close to 1 so rank correlation coefficient unchanged.
(e) H_0: $\rho = 0$, H_1: $\rho \neq 0$, critical value 0.6485
Reject H_0.

20 (a) Each box has an equal chance of being opened – we would expect each box to be opened 20 times.
(b) $\chi^2_4(5\%) = 9.488, \chi^2 = 2.3$
No reason to reject H_0. A discrete uniform distribution could be a good model.

21 (a) $S_{xy} = 6540, S_{xx} = 255\,450, \bar{y} = 16,$
$\bar{x} = 435$
(b) $y = 0.0256x + 4.863$

(c) 4.863 represents the cars likely to be sold with no advertising. 0.0256 represents the increase in car sales per £1 of advertisement.

(d) 12.5–13

22 (a) 0.72

(b) $\chi_2^2(5\%) = 5.991, \chi^2 = 2.62$

No reason to reject H_0. The B(0.72) could be a good model.

23 H_0: $\rho = 0$, $r_s = 0.8285...$, $\Sigma d^2 = 6$

More data are needed to make a decision on correlation since r_s is at the critical value.

24 (a) 4.28

(b) $\chi_4^2(5\%) = 9.488, \chi^2 = 1.18$

No reason to reject H_0. B(4.28) could be a good model.

25 $\Sigma d^2 = 78$, $r_s = 0.527...$, critical value $= 0.5636$.

The evidence is not conclusive.

26 $\chi_2^2(5\%) = 5.991, \chi^2 = 4.74...$

No reason to reject H_0.

27 (a) $\chi_3^2(5\%) = 7.815, \chi^2 = 32.15$

Reject H_0. B(0.05) is not a good model.

(b) $\rho = 0.08, \chi_3^2(5\%) = 7.815, \chi^2 = 2.22...$

Do not reject H_0. B(0.08) could be a good model.

28 (a)Points close to a straight line, x is independent of y.

(b) $S_{xy} = 2813.6, S_{xx} = 284.3999$,

$\bar{y} = 123.4, \bar{x} = 11.6\, y = 8.64 + 9.89x$

(c) slope – average daily subsistence costs

intercept – average travel cost unrelated to length of trip

(d) £117.4...

(e) 2 months is outside the range of the model so you would not use the line to find the expected expenditure.

29 $\chi_3^2(5\%) = 7.815, \chi^2 = 7.28$

Do not reject H_0.

30 (b) $S_{xx} = 2110.77$, $S_{yy} = 2894$,

$S_{xy} = 1322$, $r = 0.5348...$

(c) Some correlation – it would be better without F, J and K.

(d) $\Sigma d^2 = 34$, $r_s = 0.7939...$

(e) H_0: $\rho = 0$, H_1:$\rho > 0$, critical value $= 0.5636$

Reject H_0. The higher the aptitude mark, the higher the statistics mark is likely to be.

31 (c) $c = 2.09x - 4105$. [x is year]

(d) Since we are extrapolating we assume no major changes in drinking habits (caused by tax changes, etc.).

41.56

32 $\chi_5^2(5\%) = 11.070, \chi^2 = 2.36$

No reason to reject H_0. The data could be modelled by a continuous uniform distribution.

33 (b) Points are approximately on a straight line; x does not depend on y.

(c) $S_{xy} = 6157.584, S_{xx} = 6372.916$,

$\bar{y} = 61.083, \bar{x} = 42.416$, $y = 0.966x - 20.1$

(d) a – fixed cost (overheads), b – variable cost (manufacturing costs)

(e) 31 703 – 31 704. Break-even point.

34 $\chi_4^2(5\%) = 9.488$, $\chi^2 = 2.59...$

No reason to reject H_0. No reason to believe B(0.15) is not a good model.

35 (a) $\Sigma d^2 = 16$, $r_s = 0.714...$

(b) Critical value (5%) 0.7143,

H_0:$\rho = 0$, H_1:$\rho > 0$

Reject H_0. At this level there is reason to believe that the expert can date pottery.

36 $\chi_3^2(5\%) = 7.815, \chi^2 = 3.99$.
Do not reject H_0. There is no reason to believe that the defect rate is not the same for all machines.

37 (b) $S_{xx} = 255.6, S_{yy} = 4084.898$, $S_{xy} = 982.200$, $r = 0.961...$
(c) Strong positive correlation. The more hours of study the higher the exam mark.
(d) Data close to straight line with positive gradient.

38 (b) $S_{xx} = 1\,201\,156, S_{yy} = 130.22$, $S_{xy} = -12\,198.89$, $r = -0.975$.
(c) Strong negative correlation. As height increases temperature decreases.
(d) $H_0{:}\rho = 0$ (no association between hours of sunshine and temperature)
$H_1{:}\rho = 0$, critical value $= 0.7000$
$0.767 > 0.7000$ – reject H_0. There is an association between hours of sunshine and temperature.

39 (b) $S_{xy} = 141, S_{xx} = 17.5, \bar{y} = 35$, $\bar{x} = 2.5, y = 8.06x + 14.86$
(c) 39.03 tonnes
(d) 703 is well outside the range of the given data. It would be unwise to use the equation to estimate the yield.

40 $\chi_8^2(5\%) = 15.507, \chi^2 = 29.28$
Reject H_0. The people do not choose their numbers at random.

41 (a) $\Sigma d^2 = 56$, $r_s = 0.660...$
(b) $H_0{:}\rho = 0$, $H_1{:}\rho > 0$, critical value 0.5636
Reject H_0. There is a degree of agreement between the jumps.

42 $\chi_7^2(5\%) = 14.067, \chi^2 = 4.77...$
No reason to reject H_0. The number of bacteria could be modelled by Po(3).

43 (a) Data given in rank/place order: a significance test is required and the populations are not jointly normal, etc.
(b) $\Sigma d^2 = 28$, $r_s = 0.766...$
$H_0{:}\rho = 0$, $H_1{:}\rho > 0$, $2\frac{1}{2}\%$ critical value $= 0.7000$
Reject H_0. Tutors appear to show a reasonable level of agreement.

44 (a) The mean calculated from the data is close to 4.
(b) $\chi_8^2(5\%) = 12.592, \chi^2 = 11.634$

$11.634 < 12.592$
No reason to reject H_0.
The number of defectives could be modelled by Po(4).

45 (a) $\Sigma d^2 = 58$, $r_s = 0.648...$
(b) The null hypothesis is only rejected in favour of the alternative hypothesis if by doing so the probability of being wrong is less than or equal to the significance level.

46 (a) $\chi_3^2(5\%) = 7.815, \chi^2 = 2.92...$
No reason to reject H_0.
$N(2.7, 0.274^2)$ could be a good model.
(b) 816–817

47 (a) See 45(b)
(b) $\Sigma d^2 = 48$, $r_s = 0.4285...$
There is only a small degree of positive correlation between league position and home attendance.

48 $\mu = 434.3, \sigma = 14.3023$
$\chi_3^2(5\%) = 7.815, \chi^2 = 9.8$
Reject H_0. $N(434.3, 14.3023^2)$ is not a good model.

49 (a) $S_{xx} = 12, S_{yy} = 13.7755, S_{xy} = 13.5$
$r = 0.972...$
(b) $\Sigma d^2 = 26, r_s = 0.783...$
(c) Critical value 0.6 (one-tailed). Reject H_0. The boy's results are positively correlated with the true order – a good guess.

50 (a) $\Sigma \varepsilon_i$
(b) $S_{xy} = 258.9998, S_{xx} = 5516, \bar{y} = 5.8, \bar{x} = 42, y = 7.77 - 0.05x$
(c) 5.8 units
(d) It is better to use wood with a low moisture content.

Examination style paper T2

1 0.055

2 (a) Stratified
(b) 3 from 00 → 07; 07, 05, 04
9 from 00 → 23; 13, 19, 20, 12, 09, 17, 21, 03, 00

3 (a) (100.3, 104.5)
(b) 100 not in interval so reject claim. Customers unlikely to complain since they receive more than expected.
(c) 20

4 $\chi^2 = 2.98$, not sig., no evidence of association.

5 (a) 0.588 (b) Sig.
(c) Strong correlation suggests one test would do. Not very strong so there may be an element of difference between the tests.

6 (a) $y = 0.93 + 1.11x$
(b) 0.93 → regardless of advertising 930 copies sold
1.11 → for every £100 spent 1110 books sold.
(c) $\frac{5092}{3}$
(d) $(y - 3.6) = 1.11(x - 2.4)$
$\left.\begin{array}{l} 1.11 > 0.25 \\ 0.93 < 3.00 \end{array}\right\}$ Textbooks slow start but more rapid increase but novels start well and slow down.

7 (a) $X \geqslant c$ (b) $X \geqslant 5$ (c) 0.053
(d) 0.629
(e) Not in the critical region, no evidence to reject H_0.

8 (a) $\chi^2 = 11.8$, sig., B(5, 0.5) is not a good model.
(b) 0.488
(c) Binomial is not a good model.
(d) Number of females born is not independent – perhaps due to twins, etc.

List of symbols and notation

The following symbols and notation are used in the London modular mathematics examinations:

$\{\quad\}$	the set of
$\mathrm{n}(A)$	the number of elements in the set A
$\{x: \quad\}$	the set of all x such that
$\in$	is an element of
$\notin$	is not an element of
$\varnothing$	the empty (null) set
$\mathscr{E}$	the universal set
$\cup$	union
$\cap$	intersection
$\subset$	is a subset of
A'	the complement of the set A
PQ	operation Q followed by operation P
$\mathrm{f}: A \to B$	f is a function under which each element of set A has an image in set B
$\mathrm{f}: x \mapsto y$	f is a function under which x is mapped to y
$\mathrm{f}(x)$	the image of x under the function f
f^{-1}	the inverse relation of the function f
fg	the function f of the function g
o—o—o	open interval on the number line
●—●—●	closed interval on the number line
$\mathbb{N}$	the set of positive integers and zero, $\{0, 1, 2, 3, \ldots\}$
$\mathbb{Z}$	the set of integers, $\{0, \pm 1, \pm 2, \pm 3, \ldots\}$
$\mathbb{Z}^+$	the set of positive integers, $\{1, 2, 3, \ldots\}$
$\mathbb{Q}$	the set of rational numbers
$\mathbb{Q}^+$	the set of positive rational numbers, $\{x : x \in \mathbb{Q}, x > 0\}$
$\mathbb{R}$	the set of real numbers
$\mathbb{R}^+$	the set of positive real numbers, $\{x : x \in \mathbb{R}, x > 0\}$
$\mathbb{R}_0^+$	the set of positive real numbers and zero, $\{x : x \in \mathbb{R}, x \geqslant 0\}$
$\mathbb{C}$	the set of complex numbers
$\sqrt{\ }$	the positive square root
$[a, b]$	the interval $\{x : a \leqslant x \leqslant b\}$
$(a, b]$	the interval $\{x : a < x \leqslant b\}$
(a, b)	the interval $\{x : a < x < b\}$

$\lvert x\rvert$	the modulus of $x = \begin{cases} x \text{ for } x \geqslant 0 \\ -x \text{ for } x < 0 \end{cases}, x \in \mathbb{R}$
$\approx$	is approximately equal to
A^{-1}	the inverse of the non-singular matrix A
A^{T}	the transpose of the matrix A
det A	the determinant of the square matrix A
$\sum_{r=1}^{n} \mathrm{f}(r)$	$\mathrm{f}(1) + \mathrm{f}(2) + \ldots + \mathrm{f}(n)$
$\prod_{r=1}^{n} \mathrm{f}(r)$	$\mathrm{f}(1)\mathrm{f}(2)\ldots\mathrm{f}(n)$
$\binom{n}{r}$	the binomial coefficient $\begin{cases} \dfrac{n!}{r!(n-r)!} \text{ for } n \in \mathbb{Z}^+ \\ \dfrac{n(n-1)\ldots(n-r+1)}{r!} \text{ for } n \in \mathbb{Q} \end{cases}$
$\exp x$	e^x
$\ln x$	the natural logarithm of $x, \log_{\mathrm{e}} x$
$\lg x$	the common logarithm of $x, \log_{10} x$
arcsin	the inverse function of sin with range $[-\pi/2, \pi/2]$
arccos	the inverse function of cos with range $[0, \pi]$
arctan	the inverse function of tan with range $(-\pi/2, \pi/2)$
arsinh	the inverse function of sinh with range $\mathbb{R}$
arcosh	the inverse function of cosh with range $\mathbb{R}_0^+$
artanh	the inverse function of tanh with range $\mathbb{R}$
$\mathrm{f}'(x), \mathrm{f}''(x), \mathrm{f}'''(x)$	the first, second and third derivatives of $\mathrm{f}(x)$ with respect to x
$\mathrm{f}^{(r)}(x)$	the rth derivative of $\mathrm{f}(x)$ with respect to x
$\dot{x}, \ddot{x}, \ldots$	the first, second, . . . derivatives of x with respect to t
z	a complex number, $z = x + \mathrm{i}y = r(\cos\theta + \mathrm{i}\sin\theta) = r\mathrm{e}^{\mathrm{i}\theta}$
Re z	the real part of z, Re $z = x = r\cos\theta$
Im z	the imaginary part of z, Im $z = y = r\sin\theta$
z^*	the conjugate of $z, z^* = x - \mathrm{i}y = r(\cos\theta - \mathrm{i}\sin\theta) = r\mathrm{e}^{-\mathrm{i}\theta}$
$\lvert z\rvert$	the modulus of $z, \lvert z\rvert = \sqrt{(x^2 + y^2)} = r$
arg z	the principal value of the argument of z, arg $z = \theta$, where $\left.\begin{matrix} \sin\theta = y/r \\ \cos\theta = x/r \end{matrix}\right\} -\pi < \theta \leqslant \pi$
a	the vector **a**
$\overrightarrow{AB}$	the vector represented in magnitude and direction by the directed line segment AB
$\hat{\mathbf{a}}$	a unit vector in the direction of **a**
i,j,k	unit vectors in the directions of the cartesian coordinate axes
$\lvert\mathbf{a}\rvert$	the magnitude of **a**
$\lvert\overrightarrow{AB}\rvert$	the magnitude of $\overrightarrow{AB}$
a.b	the scalar product of **a** and **b**
$\mathbf{a} \times \mathbf{b}$	the vector product of **a** and **b**

A'	the complement of the event A
$\mathrm{P}(A)$	probability of the event A
$\mathrm{P}(A\|B)$	probability of the event A conditional on the event B
$\mathrm{E}(X)$	the mean (expectation, expected value) of the random variable X
X, Y, R, etc.	random variables
x, y, r, etc.	values of the random variables X, Y, R, etc.
$x_1, x_2 \ldots$	observations
$f_1, f_2, \ldots$	frequencies with which the observations $x_1, x_2, \ldots$ occur
$\mathrm{p}(x)$	probability function $\mathrm{P}(X = x)$ of the discrete random variable X
$p_1, p_2, \ldots$	probabilities of the values $x_1, x_2, \ldots$ of the discrete random variable X
$\mathrm{f}(x), \mathrm{g}(x), \ldots$	the value of the probability density function of a continuous random variable X
$\mathrm{F}(x), \mathrm{G}(x), \ldots$	the value of the (cumulative) distribution function $\mathrm{P}(X \leqslant x)$ of a continuous random variable X
$\mathrm{Var}(X)$	variance of the random variable X
$\mathrm{B}(n, p)$	binomial distribution with parameters n and p
$\mathrm{N}(\mu, \sigma^2)$	normal distribution with mean μ and variance σ^2
μ	population mean
σ^2	population variance
σ	population standard deviation
$\bar{x}$	sample mean
s^2	unbiased estimate of population variance from a sample, $s^2 = \frac{1}{n-1}\sum(x - \bar{x})^2$
ϕ	probability density function of the standardised normal variable with distribution N(0, 1)
Φ	corresponding cumulative distribution function
α, β	regression coefficients
ρ	product-moment correlation coefficient for a population
r	product-moment correlation coefficient for a sample
$\sim p$	not p
$p \Rightarrow q$	p implies q (if p then q)
$p \Leftrightarrow q$	p implies and is implied by q (p is equivalent to q)

Index